HOME WORKSHOP
HINTS AND TIPS

Home Workshop Hints and Tips

Edited by
Vic Smeed

NEXUS SPECIAL INTERESTS

Nexus Special Interests Ltd.
Nexus House
Boundary Way
Hemel Hempstead
Hertfordshire HP2 7ST
England

First published by Nexus Special Interests 1997

© in this collection Nexus Special Interests 1997

ISBN 1-85486-145-X

Phototypesetting by The Studio, Exeter
Printed and bound in Great Britain by Biddles Ltd., Guildford & King's Lynn

Contents

Introduction	1
SECTION 1 Lathes and Lathework	3
Removable Nose for a Mandrel	3
Centre with Tool-setting Peg	4
Divider for a Portass	4
Tapers	4
Cutting Metric Threads	6
Forming and Finishing a Screwthread	10
Cutting Square Threads	14
Packing	16
Lathe Carrier	16
Lathe Centre Gauge and Scriber	17
Sensitive Drilling Attachment	18
Boring and Facing Tools	18
Collet Chucks	20
Second Operation Set-ups	22
Boring Recesses	23
Lathe Toolposts	24
A High Speed Turning Hint	25
A Simple Lead Screw Chip Guard	26
Clasp Nut Engagement Stop	26
Simple Tool	29
Improvised Steady	29
Screwcutting B.A. Threads	29
Setting Lathe to Turn Parallel	30
How to Plane Small Gears	30
A Centre-spacing Punching Tool	32
Boring Bar Attachment	33
Turning and Boring Phosphor Bronze	33
Query – Form Tool of Complicated Shape	34

Curing the "Incurable Chuck" 34
Tightening Adjusting Screws on Cross Slides of Small Lathes 35
Cutting Multi-thread Screws 35
Query — Knurling Troubles 35
Twisted Rods 36
A Chuck for Small Screws 36
Overcoming the Deficiencies of Inaccurate Machine Tools 37
Making Screws 40

SECTION 2 Benchwork 45
Hints on Filing 45
File Cleaning 46
The Art of Drilling Holes 46
Winding Small Springs 47
Prevent of Noise 48
Small Bends, Sets and Joggles 48
Adjustable Wire-bending Tool 52
Winding Helical Springs 53
Working Pipes and Tubes 53
Mandrel for Cutting Rings from Thin Tubing 55
Adjustable Jig for Drilling Round Stock 56
Handling Small Nuts 56
Fixing Small Rivets 56
A Simple Marking Gauge 56
Toolmaker's Cramps 57
Gear Wheel Repairs 57
Chisels from Needle Files 58
Vee Supports 58
Vice to Set Small Studs 60
Cultivating Caliper Accuracy 60
Wood Lathe Bow Nuts 61
Sharpening Small Twist Drills 62
Drilling Hexagonal Holes 64
Query — Holes in Thin Sheet Metal 65
Square-ending a Drilled Hole 66
Straightedge and Surface Plate 66
Query — Scraping Planed Plates 68
Non-slip Tap Wrench 68
To Save Broken Taps 70
Simple Tap Wrench 70
Tap Grinding and Binding 71
Lubricants for Tapping 71
Some Causes of Taps Breaking 71
Cross-drilling Shafts in Vice 72
Hacksaw and Scratch Brush Hints 72
Uses for Powdered Graphite 72

vi

Drilling Laminations   73
A Handy Drilling Jig for Joint Pins, Round Bars, etc.   73
Removing Broken Taps and Drills from Castings   73
A Simple Hole-chamfering Tool   74
Holding Hacksaw Blade for Depth Slotting   75

SECTION 3   Machine Tools and Accessories   77
Spigot Cutter for Shouldering Rods   77
Tip from Canada   77
Small Bench Grinder   77
A Tip in Grinding Copper   80
Safety Washer for Grinding-wheel Spindle Nut   81
Freehand Grinding   81
Oiling Lathes and Machine Tools   83
Jointing Band Saw Blades   83
Query – Drilling Machine Chatter   84
Gripping Slips for the Machine Vice   84
Simple Belt Tensioning Device   85
Belt Dressings   85

SECTION 4   Electrical   87
Electrical Heating Elements   87
Query – Motor Trouble   89
Query – Running Cable to Workshop Motor   90
Query – Pressure-operated Switch   90
Query – Dynamo Not Working After Repair   91
Query – Wrong Direction   92
Query – Small Solenoids   92
Query – Horsepower of Motor   93

SECTION 5   Miscellaneous   95
Safety in the Workshop   95
Chemical Colouring of Metals   96
What Metal Is It?   96
Making Oilcans   102
Make Your Own Modelling Clay   102
Query – Sand for Moulding   103
Hand Cream   103
P.T.F.E.   104
Metric System   105
A Simple Forge   107
A Simple Furnace   107
Casting Aluminium Alloys   108
Melting Aluminium   110
Measurement of High Temperatures   110
Low-temperature Solders   111

Query – Glass Grinding   111
Nameplates   112
Query – Marking Steel Tools   112
Extracting a Tight Pinion   112
Query – Etching Brass   113
A Simple Method of Making Clock Hands   113
Making and Using Case-Hardening Compound   113
A Home Made Lubricant   114
Planishing Sheet Metal   115

Introduction

When the far-sighted Percival Marshall founded *The Model Engineer and Amateur Electrician* in January 1898 it was, to paraphrase his words, in recognition of the army of workers whose tastes lay in the direction of mechanics and electricity having no journal devoted to the subjects from the amateur's point of view. At that time most people were more familiar with horses than machines and the internal combustion engine and electricity, which would in time supplant wind, water and steam as major power sources, were relatively recent innovations. There were engineers in industry who could pursue their interest in spare time, using knowledge acquired at work, but there were far more potential enthusiasts who had no mechanical background and needed education and guidance, both provided in abundance by the magazine at just twopence a week!

As electricity grew to become taken for granted and its widespread use created an ever-expanding market for mass-produced equipment, the necessity or incentive for amateur construction diminished and the 'Amateur Electrician' part of the title was discontinued. The 'Model' aspect of the title reflects the fact that an engineering model requires much the same machinery and techniques as full-size prototypes, but on a scale and with work sizes more suited to the home workshop. To make something which functions gives point to those who enjoy working with metal as a hobby; their materials and methods are also shared with professionals who earn their living from the output of small machine shops.

Over the years an enormous amount of useful information has been published, from lengthy series of articles by eminent engineers to brief tips from average enthusiasts. Some of this material has subsequently appeared in book form, but most lies undiscovered by those who do not easily have access to early issues. This book is, effectively, a random dip into the middle fifty years of the magazine, offering an assortment of ideas relating to general metalwork, with the emphasis on lathe usage and benchwork and an occasional glimpse of practices now not so frequently encountered. It is hoped that at least some of the items will be of use and interests to readers of any degree of experience.

1

Lathes and Lathework

Removable Nose for a Mandrel

H.S. Wheeler (November 1964)

A useful addition to a Myford ML7 lathe is a removable nose for the outer end of the mandrel. I found it quite simple to make.

It consists of a nosepiece which is a replica of the standard mandrel nose, and an extending neck which is stepped. The $\frac{3}{4}$ in. dia. step passes through the hole in the gear guard and forms a stop at the end of the mandrel. The end of the smaller $\frac{19}{32}$ in. dia. step is sawcut and coned out, and a mating cone is made.

A $\frac{5}{16}$ in. dia. clearing hole is drilled right through the attachment and in this is passed a long stud, screwed $\frac{5}{16}$ in. Whitworth at each end.

To assemble the device on the lathe we need only push it right home in the mandrel and then tighten the external nut, which draws the cone into the taper and expands the end of the stepped part. The clamping is quite rigid.

If the standard faceplate is now screwed on the nose part, it will be very useful for turning the mandrel by hand, as in small screwing or tapping operations. By securing the appropriate disc to the faceplate you can also use the device for sanding or finishing, by running the lathe at top speed. The mandrel should then be run in reverse, to prevent the possibility

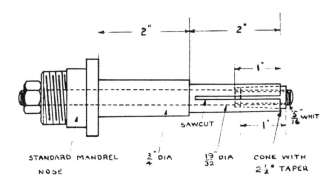

STANDARD MANDREL NOSE $\frac{3}{4}$" DIA $\frac{19}{32}$" DIA   CONE WITH $2\frac{1}{2}$° TAPER

that the faceplate will unscrew.

It will save you the removal of a good deal of stock if you make the nosepiece and stepped tailpiece separately and then screw and pin the tailpiece into the nosepiece. You can remove the device instantly by slackening off the external nut and giving the spindle a light tap to clear the tapered cone, when the whole can be pulled out.

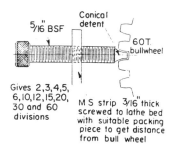

Gives 2,3,4,5, 6,10,12,15,20, 30 and 60 divisions

M S strip 3/16" thick screwed to lathe bed with suitable packing piece to get distance from bull wheel

Centre with Tool-setting Peg
(January 1924)

The appended view represents an idea for tool-setting down to quite small diameters by the use of a peg inserted in a cross-hole in a special back-centre. The latter should be cut away as shown so that the tool may pass along when the peg is set only to a small amount of projection.

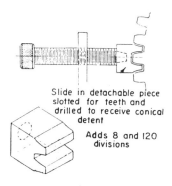

Slide in detachable piece slotted for teeth and drilled to receive conical detent

Adds 8 and 120 divisions

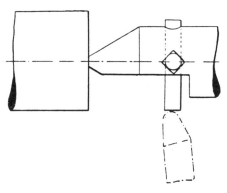

Divider for a Portass
A.G. Allnut (April 1964)

Readers with a Portass or similar lathe may be interested in my divider, if they have a 60t bull wheel. The conical shape detent is, perhaps, not perfect but it works well enough.

Tapers
'Geometer' (January 1957)

The desirable true running of a pulley or flywheel taper-fitted on a shaft is generally best ensured by finishing faces and outside diameter with the component mounted on a mandrel running between centres in the lathe. All important surfaces are thus finished at one setting and the wheel is both parallel and concentric—a condition difficult to achieve by chucking and re-chucking no matter how carefully this may be done.

The preliminary roughing out is advisedly done in a chuck (which can be a four-jaw independent type with the jaws reversed if necessary, since heavier cuts can be taken in a chuck than on a mandrel) leaving about 1/64 in. surplus for finishing. In this way, scale or any hard spots in the casting can be successfully dealt with in the rough machining, using a slow rotational speed and taking cuts deep enough to be everywhere well below the surface.

Diagrams A and B illustrate typical chuck set-ups for rough machining a small flywheel, the material removed at each being shown by the shaded areas. At each set-up the wheel is pushed back to the jaws for facial alignment, and the jaws are regulated for peripheral or general spinning truth.

Although it is not vital to do so, it is generally best to machine the taper bore on the first set-up, and also to turn along the outside diameter as far as possible. On the second set-up it is then practicable to fit a taper mandrel in the bore and employ its end for checking and truing — if it should happen that it is difficult to apply the pointer of a surface gauge to a portion of the outside diameter.

Moreover, should a small error result from the setting, cleaning cuts can easily be taken on the mandrel set-up C since the particular faces will be towards the tailstock.

Taper uniformity

When the shaft is available on which the wheel is to fit, it can be tried in the taper as this is machined (or reamed) in order to locate the wheel endwise correctly — in which respect, should the taper bore be made slightly too large a reducing cut can always be taken over the face.

Alternatively, the bore can be sized from a reamer or mandrel, as at D, which may be necessary if the component is a replacement, or one is requiring to standardise tapers for wheels to be fitted on different shafts. In the case of a mandrel, a shoulder can be left in machining or a

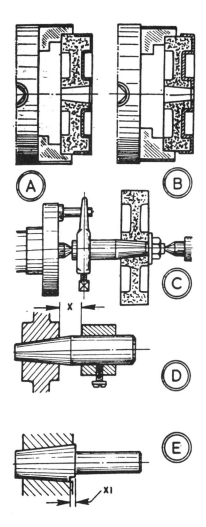

sleeve can be fitted for a distance X to obtain when the taper is at correct size; in the case of a reamer, a sleeve is essential when the distance can be measured with a rule, or a small gauge made just to push into the space.

A common type of gauge for this method of sizing tapers is as E, where the taper

5

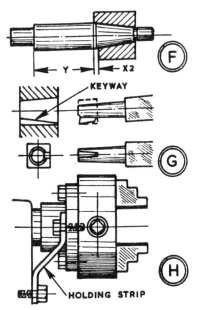

KEYWAY

G

H

HOLDING STRIP

portion ends in a step on one side *X1*. On the tool being pushed tightly into the bore to be tested, the step should go just below the surface while the full diameter just stands proud—showing the bore to be within its particular tolerance.

Should the gauge enter too far a light correcting cut can always be taken across the face—assuming there remains sufficient material on other faces to machine them into relationship—which is as good a reason as any for finishing the taper early in the proceedings.

The principle also applies to a shaft *F* where a ring gauge (corresponding to the component) is used. This may have a step *X2* to locate the position where the taper finishes at the full diameter, or at the opposite end on the small diameter, though a better way is to take the distance *Y* from the face to a shoulder or the end of the shaft.

If a keyway is required in a wheel its cutting should be the final operation. From square silver steel a tool is made as *G*, turning the shank, filing the surplus to tool shape, then hardening and tempering. Planing cuts are taken from the saddle with the chuck secured against rotation, as at *H*, by a holding strip from backplate to headstock.

Cutting Metric Threads
The use of a 127-toothed wheel for metric screwcutting on an English lathe
By Geo. Gentry (July 1955)

This article relates to a problem which is constantly recurring in both amateur and professional workshops, and it is proposed to deal with it in some detail to satisfy the requirements of querists who have asked for advice on how to produce metric threads on lathes with fractional-inch pitch lead screws. In the particular instances, the pitch of the lead screw is not specified, but it will be assumed that it is 8 t.p.i., as this is the pitch most commonly employed on English lathes of the sizes employed by model engineers. Neither is it known what change wheels may be available, but if the basic principles of the calculations are grasped, they can be adapted to different lead screws or change wheels by the use of elementary arithmetic.

Ratio of wheel numbers

If the pitch of a screw to be cut is given, the ratio of gearing required is expressed as the ratio of the pitch to be cut (on the mandrel end) to the pitch of the lead-screw (on its appropriate end). If, however, the reciprocal of the pitch be given (i.e. number of threads per inch), the reciprocal of the lead screw pitch is put on the mandrel, and the screw to be cut on the leadscrew. In the first case, as an example, if it is desired to cut a pitch of 1 mm. with a leadscrew of $2\frac{1}{2}$ mm., the ratio of gears will be $1/2\frac{1}{2}$ or 1 to $2\frac{1}{2}$ mandrel to screw.

In the second case, if it is desired to cut 12 t.p.i. with a lead screw of 8 t.p.i., the ratio of gears will be 8/12 or 8 to 12 mandrel to screw.

Applying the second case, to explain the use of the 127 wheel, it is necessary to know that there are 25.4 mm. in 1 in., or a 1 mm. pitch screw may be expressed as 25.4 t.p.i. This is not *exactly* correct but has only an error of the order of two millionths of an inch in an inch which is negligible entirely.

If then we require to cut 25.4 t.p.i. with a leadscrew of 8 t.p.i., applying the second case, the ratio of gears will be 8/25.4 or 8 to 25.4 mandrel to screw. Thus:

$$\frac{8}{25.4} \times \frac{5}{5} = \frac{40}{127}$$

the smallest factor which can be used to bring 25.4 to whole numbers being 5. Thus a simple train (i.e. *not* a compound train) made with a 40 wheel on mandrel end and 127 wheel on the 8 t.p.i. lead-screw end will cut 25.4 t.p.i. or 1 mm. pitch (Fig. 1). Forty is the driver and 127 the driven or follower of the train.

Keeping to simple trains throughout and retaining the 127 on the screw, the 40 wheel must be replaced with wheels corresponding to the fractions of mm. pitch or multipliers of mm. pitch required. Thus to cut $\frac{1}{2}$ mm. pitch, $\frac{1}{2}$ of 40 or 20 will be required on mandrel as a driver. To cut 0.6 mm. pitch 0.6 of 40 = 24 wheel will be required and to cut 0.7 mm. 0.7 of 40 = 28 wheel will be required and none others, if *simple* trains are required. This explains the following table, a study of which will explain that to cut fractions of mm. we speed down the

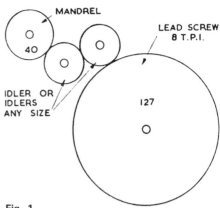

Fig. 1

screw and to cut over 1 mm. speed up the same. The use of idle wheels is given at the end of this article.

Compound trains

To make clear the principle of compounding, which will be necessary in some cases where the drivers given are not available, the interested reader must understand the idea of speeding down or up in proportion to the fraction or multiplier of 1 mm. required to be cut. If, for instance, $\frac{1}{2}$ mm. is required and no 20 wheel is available, the compounding wheels must have the ratio 2 to 1 down, say 48 and 24, thus retaining the original 40 driver, put it 40 driving into 48 on intermediate stud and 24 keyed to 48 on same (and running with it) driving the 127 on screw (Fig. 2).

If there should be trouble in getting the wheels to come together, the 24 and 40 drivers may be changed about, giving 24 on mandrel driving 48 on stud, and 40 on stud (keyed to 48) driving 127 on screw. If, however, 24 and 48 are either or both not available:
56 and 28; 60 and 30; 64 and 32

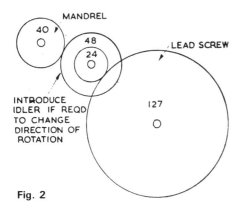

Fig. 2

or any 2 to 1 wheels available may be used in the same way. Applying the principle where 0.6 mm. is required and no 24 is available, the compounding wheels must have the ratio 1 to 0.6 down or 10 to 6, say wheels 50 to 30 giving 40 driving 50 on stud and 30 keyed to 50 driving 127 on screw.

Then, again, if it is required to cut 2 mm. pitch and there is no 2 × 40 = 80 available, speed up the train 1 to 2. Thus, using 24 and 48: with 40 on mandrel driving 24 on stud and 48 keyed to 24 on stud driving 127 on screw will do it (Fig. 3). In this case, however, it may be necessary to change the 48 and 40 driver about, giving 48 on mandrel

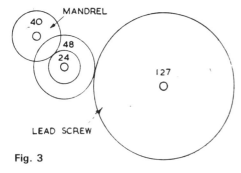

Fig. 3

driving 24 on stud, and 40 keyed to 24 driving the 127 on screw.

It is obviously impossible to prepare a correct compound table in the absence of knowledge of wheels available, but readers are advised to master the principle, and having got a correct working setting to note down the wheels used and ultimately complete their own table for reference.

There is one other instance. Say it is necessary to cut $1\frac{1}{2}$ mm. pitch and there is no 60 available. Keeping the 40 on mandrel, speed up 1 to $1\frac{1}{2}$ using say 20 to 30. That is 40 on mandrel, driving 20 on stud and 30 keyed to 20 driving 127 on screw.

It may be that the simple train driver is too large, even though wheels may be available; as, for instance, the use of 100 into 127, and so make useless any intermediate idle wheel or wheels. In such a case, gear *down* 2 to 1 by using 50 as a driver and then counter-gear *up* by compounding 1 to 2 with any pair. Say 20 and 40. Thus 50 on mandrel driving 20 on stud and 40 on stud (keyed to 20) driving 127 on screw will cut $2\frac{1}{2}$ mm.

In compounding, where it is necessary to use idle wheels in a corresponding simple train to preserve the right direction of rotation, the compounding wheels serve the purpose of one *idle* wheel.

General requirements

The novice at setting up screwcutting trains must realise that in arranging a compound train, double-width intermediate studs are necessary, and a double-width nose on lead screw. Idle wheels may have any number of teeth. If the lead screw has a right-hand thread, the mandrel and lead screw must revolve in the same direction to cut a right-hand thread.

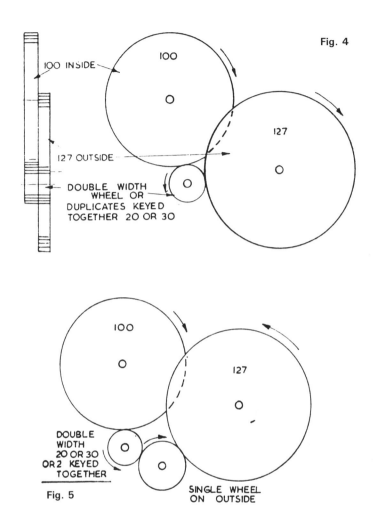

Fig. 4

100 INSIDE

100

127

127 OUTSIDE

DOUBLE WIDTH WHEEL OR DUPLICATES KEYED TOGETHER 20 OR 30

100

127

DOUBLE WIDTH 20 OR 30 OR 2 KEYED TOGETHER

SINGLE WHEEL ON OUTSIDE

Fig. 5

Unless a cluster gear or other means of reversing the gear train are provided, therefore, one idler gear between mandrel and lead screw must be used; for left-hand threads, two idlers are necessary.

Difficulty in setting up a gear train may arise when wheels which do not mesh with each other overlap owing to their large diameter. This may occur when using, say, a 100 wheel on the mandrel and a 127 on the lead screw. It may be overcome by using an idler of double width, or two wheels of the same size keyed together, as in Fig. 4; to reverse the direction, a second idler is added, as in Fig. 5. These conditions apply to all screwcutting trains, quite apart from those used for cutting metric threads.

mm.	Fractions of mm.	Mandrel wheel	Idlers	Lead screw wheel
0.5	1/2	20	Any no. of teeth	127
0.6	3/5	24	"	"
0.7	7/10	28	"	"
0.75	3/4	30	"	"
0.8	4/5	32	"	"
0.85	17/20	34	"	"
0.9	9/10	36	"	"
1.0	1	40	"	"
1.1	1 1/10	44	"	"
1.2	1 1/5	48	"	"
1.25	1 1/4	50	"	"
1.3	1 3/10	52	"	"
1.4	1 2/5	56	"	"
1.5	1 1/2	60	"	"
1.6	1 3/5	64	"	"
1.7	1 7/10	68	"	"
1.75	1 3/4	70	"	"
1.8	1 4/5	72	"	"
1.9	1 9/10	76	"	"
2.0	2	80	"	"
2.25	2 1/4	90	"	"
2.5	2 1/2	100	"	"

Forming and Finishing a Screwthread

E.T. Westbury (May 1963)

When V-threads of relatively coarse pitch are cut, the load on the tool point becomes very heavy, as the breadth of the cutting edge in action increases rapidly with the depth. Top rake, which in normal circumstances can be used to reduce loading in machining steel and other tough metals, has a limited value in screwcutting. Experienced turners sometimes ease the load on the tool by shifting it sideways slightly between cuts, using the topslide feed, and centralising it only for the final cuts. This is effective if skilfully carried out, but it can hardly be recommended as a general practice, especially for the beginner, because of the risk of disastrous error.

A well-known alternative method, which is much more certain in its results, is to swivel the topslide to the flank angle of the thread, which in the Whitworth form is $27\frac{1}{2}$ deg. from a right angle, or in other words $62\frac{1}{2}$ deg. from the lathe axis. When the tool is fed in at this angle, it cuts on the leading flank alone, and the load on the extreme point is greatly reduced. The tool may with advantage be given side rake for dealing with steel—a downward slope from the leading flank. Using the topslide for quick withdrawal of the tool at the end of the cut is not very convenient. The usual practice is to employ the cross-slide and return it to the same point each time, applying the cutting feed only on the topslide.

Some lathes, including the Myford ML7, do not provide for sufficient swivelling of the topslide. With the type of ball handle favoured (not necessarily the best, but the most popular) it is rather difficult to find room for manipulating both the cross and top feeds at this angle in lathes of limited centre height. Several devices have been described in ME for increasing the swivelling range of the ML7; they usually involve the raising of the cross-slide by a packing plate, and thus restrict the size of the tool which can be used in the normal toolpost, but there is still room to fit a tool which is quite adequate.

The generation of screwthreads in the lathe is essentially a jobbing task; it is rarely, if ever, used in quantity production as it is far too slow to suit general requirements. Except in high precision toolroom work, such as the production of screw pitch gauges, exact measurement of all thread dimensions is seldom made. Most of us, having turned the screw blank, or bored the tapping hole, to nominal dimensions, work by "fit and feel," either to a gauge or to the mating part, rather than by precise measurement. Complete specifications of thread dimensions are sometimes very complicated, as anyone will discover who looks up the BS figures. Quite apart from the hundreds of different thread pitches, there are over 180 thread forms (flank angle, root and tip radius, and effective depth) in use at present.

As a general guide for those who are mainly interested in cutting threads to Whitworth form (which embraces BSF, BSP, brass pipe, and several other British Standard pitches) the depth of thread is approximately 0.64 of the pitch. Thus for 16 t.p.i., the depth of thread is

$$\frac{0.64}{16} = 0.040 \text{ in., and for 24 t.p.i.}$$

is $\dfrac{0.64}{24} = 0.0266$ in.

It is assumed that the radius at the tip of the tool is in exact proportion to the pitch, but this is very difficult to ensure, especially when allowance for wear of the tool point must be taken into account. There is some latitude in the fit, and even the form, of most threads, and it is better to have too fine a radius than otherwise.

Unless specially ground tools for every pitch of thread are used, it is impossible to work to dead measurement of the thread depth on this assessment. The threads are therefore usually finished with chasers.

Hand and machine chasers are essentially multi-toothed form tools, of correct form and pitch for various threads. Generally speaking, machine chasers are not suited for use on light lathes; in any event they are relatively expensive, and a set of them, both outside and inside, to cover the range of pitches likely to be used would be beyond the resources of most amateur workshops. Hand chasers are cheaper and will cover most requirements in light engineering.

In the past, chasers have been much used for cutting threads from the solid blank, on lathes not otherwise equipped for screwcutting. Skill is required to manipulate them, as they must be presented to the work in a sweeping movement, related to the pitch of the thread and the speed of the lathe. Until such skill is attained, many jobs are likely to be spoiled through incorrect tracking or drunken threads. The use of a chaser to finish the form and size of a thread already generated, at least partly, is much easier, and more appropriate to presentday practice. In common with other hand turning tools, chasers should be fitted with handles long enough to give plenty of leverage. They also call for the use of a toolrest, as close to the work as possible. Unless the standard form of

11

T-rest is employed, a rigid bar must be fixed to the toolpost at a suitable height to support the chaser with its cutting edge close to lathe centre height. For external work the rest is set parallel to the lathe axis, and for internal work at right angles to it.

The surface of the rest must be smooth, so that the chaser can slide freely on it, and a little oil or grease applied to it is helpful. Sometimes the teeth on the underside of the chaser are inclined to drag; I find it advisable to round them off by grinding, but obviously care must be taken not to touch the thread form at the top cutting edge. The rounding off is also helpful if the chaser needs to be slightly tilted to cut properly, but it should always be used with the top surface as near truly radial with the work as it can be. A fierce cutting angle will tend to cause chatter or digging in and will also make the thread form too shallow.

As internal chasers must always be used with an overhang, dependent on the depth of the thread on which they are working, they should be kept resting dead flat on the toolrest, and so the height of the rest is more important than it is in outside work. The lathe speed needs to be kept fairly low—not more than about 100 r.p.m.—especially for short threads, or for running up close to a shoulder or blind end. Lubrication is necessary when you are working in steel, and is desirable for aluminium alloys, but is not needed for brass or cast iron. In the lack of special lubricants for different metals—not always very convenient in a small workshop—I find a good soluble oil, such as Shell Dromus, the most useful, as it can be diluted to suit all purposes, except the very heaviest duties.

Of threads other than the V-form, the commonest are square, acme, and buttress. The technique of generating them is much the same, except for the shape of the tool. Square threads do not generally call for very close limits at the root and crest, but should fit closely on the sides for maximum strength and the prevention of backlash. The tool needs to be carefully ground to exactly half the pitch in width and with slight, but definite, side clearance. Sometimes a narrower tool is used, and side cuts are taken after full depth has been reached; you should then make a gauge to check the width of the thread groove.

The front edge of the tool should be ground exactly square with the sides. For working on steel, top rake up to about 15 deg. is desirable. As the load on the tool point does not increase with the depth of cut, the feed applied at each pass may be constant except for one or more fine finishing cuts. The need, with coarse-pitch threads, for increased side

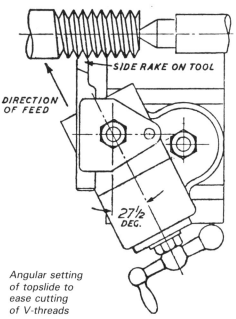

Angular setting of topslide to ease cutting of V-threads

clearance on the leading edge of the tool to conform with the helix angle of the thread is specially important in multi-start cutting. A special form of tool-holder, which enables the cutter to be partly rotated, is an advantage for this

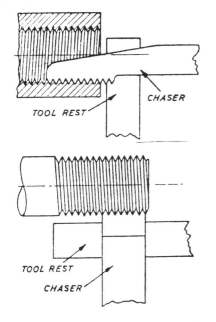

A hand chaser is used on internal threads (top) and on external ones

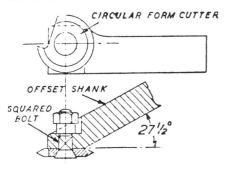

Circular screwcutting tool with offset shank

work; or the tool may be made from round bar and held in a V-packing block or split clamp to provide the same facility. Angular setting of the tool alters its effective width in relation to the axial plane of the work, and allowance must be made for this.

Acme threads have advantages over square threads for many purposes, as they are stronger at the root and have an increased area of bearing surface. They can be made a close fit both endwise and diametrically, and for leadscrews with a split clasp nut they give much easier engagement than square threads, without backlash when they are fully engaged.

The flanks of the threads have an included angle of 29 deg., and an accurately ground tool is required for forming them, though not necessarily of the exact width to form both flanks at once. To reduce load on the tool point you can gash the threads with a square thread tool slightly narrower than the root of the groove, and to within one or two thou of the finished depth.

Buttress threads have a saw-tooth or ratchet form, and are used for screws which have to sustain heavy end thrust in one direction only; their form is not rigidly standardised, and in some examples, such as in vice screws, the sheer face of the thread may be slightly undercut, so the thread tends to pull more tightly into engagement as load is applied. This thread may be cut by feeding the tool along the line of the angular flank, as for V-threads; but if the sheer flank is undercut, the tool must also be withdrawn at an angle, and not squarely, by using the crossfeed only.

Special tools of several kinds are made for screwcutting; the most useful is the circular form tool—in other words, a disc with the edge ground to the required thread form and notched to provide the cutting face. It is secured to a holder by a central bolt, and can be rotated for adjusting the height of the point, and also to compensate for regrinding, which is, of course, necessary on the top face only.

The great advantage of this tool is that it maintains the true thread form throughout its working life, and as the form can be accurately generated and highly finished it promotes equally high quality in the work produced. I made such a tool many years ago, especially for dealing with very fine threads, for which the grinding of tools is, to say the least, rather tricky. It has a squared bolt with a tapered head to hold the disc firmly, and at the same time to avoid side projections which might interfere with working close up to a shoulder. The shank is offset at $27\frac{1}{2}$ deg., so that when the topslide is set for working at flank angle, it only needs to be lined up with the edge of the slide.

In the cutting of multi-start threads and other special operations normally outside the scope of the beginner, some means of indexing the work to space the individual "starts" is needed; the alternative of shifting the cross-slide through the exact distance between them is not, in my experience, very reliable. The index must be used for measurement, and errors may occur through backlash in the slides. For work machined between centres, and driven by a carrier, a convenient method of angular indexing is by a special driving plate with provision for shifting the driving pin into the required number of equidistant positions. Chuck work is more difficult unless a special indexing backplate is employed. You do the indexing by a change wheel on the lathe mandrel or cluster shaft, taking great care not to disturb other wheels in the train when you are disengaging and re-meshing.

Every operation described in this series has been carried out by myself. It has always been my aim to pass on to readers such knowledge as I have acquired in the hardest and most expensive of all schools — experience.

Cutting Square Threads
R. Johnston (August 1964)

In the cutting of square threads the front cutting edge of the tool must be at right angles to the helix of the thread, and the tool itself can resemble a parting tool as the width of the blade should narrow slightly where it joins the stock, to provide clearance.

You must add about 0.003 in. to the width of the cutting edge so that the tool can move between the flanks of the thread when you are finally gauging the work. It is also essential that the top rake should be correct in relation to the material.

In producing a male screw, you should have a gauge or nut to hand for the final sizing. The diameter must be turned carefully and is usually reduced by 0.004 in. In starting to cut, we bring the tool forward, with the lathe turning slowly, until it is just grazing the diameter, at which point the dial on the cross-slide is set at zero. By a series of passes over the work with the lathe in correct pitch, the tool being moved two or three thou at a time, we obtain a depth of 0.125 in., or $\frac{1}{8}$ in. Having taken the thread to the depth on the dial, we should have 0.004 in. at the root, thus providing the tolerance needed for a gauge fit.

If we take the diameter to be $\frac{9}{16}$ in., the decimal size will be 0.5625 and a natural pitch for this is 4 t.p.i. We must remember that a square thread is box-like in section with all the dimensions equal.

The method which I have described

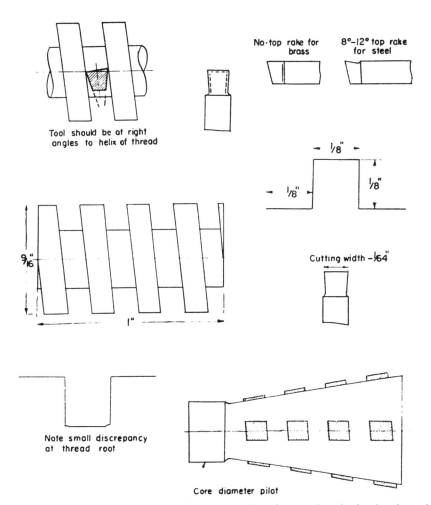

Tool should be at right
angles to helix of thread

No·top rake for
brass

8°-12° top rake
for steel

⊢ 1/8" ⊣

⊢ 1/8" ⊣   1/8"

Cutting width –1/64"

9/16"

1"

Note small discrepancy
at thread root

Core diameter pilot

*Operational details and some of the dimensions and angles are given in the drawings above.
The small diagram at top centre shows the tool profile used for roughing out.*

will take all the hazard and uncertainty out of the cutting so long as a few rules are observed. A good soluble oil should be used, particularly when steel is being cut, and the tool should be set at the correct centre height, avoiding unneces-

sary overhang. Again, you must see that all the levers and gear wheels are secure before you begin. If one of the levers slips out of gear, the work will almost certainly have to be scrapped.

In screw-cutting very tough materials

15

we use a couple of tools. The first of them is slightly smaller at the point and is known as the rougher. We take it to the root of the work, and an additional three or four thou deeper. Then we set up the finishing tool and go only to the depth, plus 0.003 in.

The smaller parallel part of the thread root is slightly uneven because the rougher is taken just a shade deeper than the finishing tool. As this does not materially affect the quality of the thread, the method is considered permissible. The discrepancy can scarcely be seen.

To cut internal square threads is not easy. As the tool employed has a sharp right-angle bend, with lack of support to oppose the cutting action, you should work only in short lengths. The accepted practice is to use a series of hand-taps, the larger sizes of which often have as many as four to a set.

Some makers provide a parallel extension on the first tap to act as a gauge to maintain the correct size.

Packing
Martin Cleeve (June 1964)

In loading or re-loading a four-tool turret, or in setting any tool to the correct centre height in a lathe (unless an adjustable height toolpost is being used), a search for packing pieces to put below the tool shanks can easily waste a good deal of time. We have our bits of hacksaw blade (giving a rather drastic increase in height), and pieces of brass strip, shim-stock and so on, but seldom any real *plan*.

I long ago decided that something should be done, and now I always keep a small tray filled with a variety of mild steel strips, $\frac{3}{8}$ in. wide, about $2\frac{1}{2}$ in. long and $\frac{1}{32}$ in. and $\frac{1}{16}$ in. thick (a few are $\frac{1}{4}$ in.). The backbone of the selection consists of perhaps three dozen strips

taken from a sheet of zinc, 17 thousandths of an inch in thickness. They are cut by being scribed and snapped off along the groove so formed, to $2\frac{1}{2}$ in. × $\frac{3}{8}$ in. These are the pieces most frequently used, not so much for the packing-up, but to restore a sharpened tool to centre height. For all but the most exacting work on very small diameters, I have found that 17 thous is not too much of a sudden increment.

Besides the packing tray, I have a tin labelled "Zinc chucking pads." Here I keep an assortment of collars made from sheet zinc, for wrapping around finished surfaces which have to be re-chucked without marking. I also have a number of spare strips for making these wrappers, the blanks being about 8 in. long and $\frac{3}{4}$ in. wide.

When certain lathe-milling jobs are being set up without a vertical slide, pieces of sheet zinc packing can be extremely useful. Zinc is soft enough to bed-down flat and easily under clamping pressure, and it puts up quite a good resistance to slipping between abutting surfaces. Finer shades of height adjustment may also be made with paper or with zinc and paper combined.

Lathe Carrier
H.H. Nicholls (January 1969)

A few days ago I had to grip a piece of screwed rod in the lathe by means of a carrier, and found I had nothing suitable for the job. A carrier was soon made, in this way: —

I scooped out a hollow in a piece of soft brick, the kind used by bricklayers for "rubbed work," (but Plaster of Paris when hard and dry would do as well), and cast the lead jaws 1, and formed the hollows to grip the work with a coarse round file.

16

Then I cut a short piece of steel, 2, and a longer piece, 3, and arranged two bolts as shown; the circle, 4, represents the driver pin of the lathe. The lead jaws were united to the steel pieces by one of the "impact" adhesives now found in every workshop, and all tightly fixed round the screwed piece as shown.

The lead did not damage the brass screw; the grip was ample to hold the work when care and very light feed were combined in doing the job.

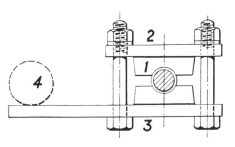

Lathe Centre Gauge and Scriber
By Jed (April 1924)

This very useful tool can be easily made, and serves the purpose of a gauge for setting the tool at centre height on the slide rest, also in lieu of a scribing block on the lathe bed, and, having a larger base, is better for marking out and setting work true in the chuck.

For marking graduations in dividing work in the lathe it is far quicker and better than a screw-cutting tool clamped on the top slide on its side. The marking point can be swivelled and set to mark either a face or edge and positioned where it is most effective.

The following sizes apply to a $3\frac{1}{2}$-in. lathe and can be varied to suit the particular machine: – Base of cast iron or wrought iron flat bar, 5 ins. by $1\frac{1}{2}$ ins. by $\frac{1}{2}$ in.

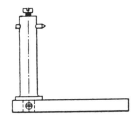

A Centre Marking Gauge for the Lathe

Face up one side dead flat and true, clamp on faceplate with the trued side down to bore the $\frac{1}{2}$-in. hole $\frac{3}{4}$ in. from one end, and face up round the hole at the same setting.

It is important that this hole and facing be true and square with each other.

Drill and tap for a $\frac{1}{4}$-in. brass screw into the $\frac{1}{2}$-in. hole edgewise through the base.

The pillar can be turned out of an old bolt or any available piece of iron. The spigot that fits the $\frac{1}{2}$ in. hole in base and the shoulder that butts on the facing round the hole must be true and a good fit.

Press the pillar well down on the facing when clamping in position by the set-screw at the side. Place a sharp-pointed centre in the lathe spindle, keep the base of the scriber on the lathe bed while drawing the pillar across the centre point to mark exact centre height. Remove the pillar and drill a 3/16th-in. hole transversely through on the mark. Drill and tap centrally endwise into this hole for a 3/16th-in. clamping screw.

The cutter is a piece of 3/16-in. round silver steel, the point filed to a triangular point about 60°, the extreme end being just a shade eccentric.

To set it to centre height, keep the base pressed down on lathe bed and rotate the cutter slowly, sighting it sideways against a sharp-pointed centre; a

17

piece of white card held behind will show up the two points and assist in the setting. When exact the cutter is clamped by the top screw, which is not again moved unless the cutter should need sharpening, all swivelling of the cutter being effected by the screw in base.

The cutter point is hardened right out in oil.

Sensitive Drilling Attachment
S.E. Capps (July 1955)

Some users of small lathes may have found that when using small drills from the tailstock, the screw feed is not as sensitive as when the ram is lever-operated. In fact, great care must be exercised when using drills below $\frac{3}{16}$ in. dia. to avoid breaking them. Below this size, the insensitivity of the screw feed becomes marked. I had this trouble, and made the attachment shown in the sketches, in preference to converting the tailstock to lever operation. As will be seen in Fig. 1, the attachment is simple, and fits the taper in the ram in place of the centre.

The body is made from mild steel turned to fit the taper in the ram and is bored to take a shaft carrying a small drill chuck, which should be a good sliding fit in the hole, without being slack. The head of the body is slotted to take a lever, which passes through a slot cut in the shaft to take it, and the end of the lever is secured in the head by a screw on which it can move freely. Note that the lever is shaped at the inner end to give it the necessary movement for small drilling, and a plastic or metal knob is fitted to the outer end of the lever for comfortable working. All the working parts should be well finished, and tool-making limits of accuracy aimed at from start to finish. If properly made, the sensitivity of the lever is such that the

Fig. 1. *The finished attachment*

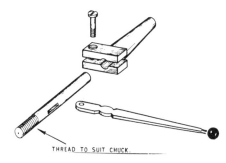

THREAD TO SUIT CHUCK.

Fig. 2. *Showing the general construction*

cutting drag of a 1/32-in. drill can be easily felt, and, of course, the withdrawal of the drill for the clearance of cuttings is instantaneous. A big advantage of the attachment is that it can be slipped into the tailstock for use in a few seconds, and used without apprehension of trouble from broken drills.

Boring and Facing Tools
'Geometer' (January 1964)

Many operations on the lathe require special tools and cutters which model engineers and professional turners in small workshops must design and make themselves. Their position differs greatly from that of machinists in large works

18

where everything is prepared by planning and production engineers. There the skill of lathe operators goes into their work; opportunities for initiative are limited.

It is different at home and in small commercial workshops. As many facilities are lacking, ingenuity is often as important as skill. You may even come to rely on a calculated blending of the two for the solution to many problems. You never forget that your ideas must cost little in terms of time and money.

The first applications of these principles are usually tools and cutters made from silver steel and tool bits—boring tools and flycutters mounted in mild steel holders, D-bits and endmills to hold in chucks. Form tools, taper reamers, Woodruff keyway cutters and so forth, come later.

Some boring tools and flycutters which are easy to make appear at diagram A. All have round holders and can be run in the chuck to machine work on the topslide or vertical slide. Type 1 can be used for rough-machining bores from the tailstock. Types 2 and 3 can be mounted in split holders on the topslide for boring work in the chuck.

Holders 1 and 2 have an advantage in strength in small sizes over holders with grub screws to secure tool bits. The end of the round stock carries a fine thread on which a nut is screwed to force the tool to the end face where it is firmly held. A double-ended cutter goes right through the nut, which can be drilled and reamed through two flats. I used a brass union nut for the first one. To hold a short tool bit, for topslide boring, a blank nut must be used, with the tool bit against its face, the end of the round stock being reduced to bear on the bit, as at 2. For long life, nuts and holders should be in mild steel, preferably case-hardened, or in hardened and tempered cast steel.

Holder 3 can be used in the two ways mentioned—in the chuck or on the topslide, the angle mounting of the tool bit allowing it to work to shoulders or end-faces. To help in drilling the hole for the bit, a small flat can be filed on the holder where the drill is to enter, and another where it will emerge. This dodge helps reaming as well.

Boring tools at B are used in the tailstock to open out cored or drilled holes before they are finished in the normal way with a tool from the topslide. The tailstock is brought up and clamped, and feed is applied through the handwheel.

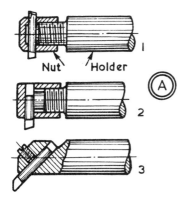

Nut Holder
(A)
1
2
3

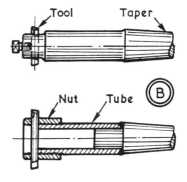

Tool Taper
Nut Tube (B)

The upper holder is in solid mild steel with a taper to fit the tailstock barrel and a grubscrew to grip the double-ended cutter. This is standard for small and medium sizes. The lower holder is built up with the cutter held in a similar way to that for holders 1 and 2 at A. It is useful in large sizes, as it reduces extension of the cutter. A threaded tube is welded or brazed to a taper shank for the tailstock and carries an open, cross-drilled nut for the cutter.

A D-bit is almost as good as a reamer to smooth and size a hole which has been drilled in work in the chuck. The tool can be easily and cheaply made from standard silver steel rod, and can be held in a chuck in the tailstock or mounted in a tapershank holder. The cutting end is shown at C1. Take care in filing and honing the flats not to take the cutting edge beneath the diameter, or the bit will seize in the bore. The tempering should be to dark straw colour after the hardening.

Double-edged cutters or endmills, of which C2 shows an example, are usually made in standard silver steel. The flats which give the cutting edges can be

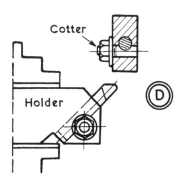

filed first like those of D-bits. Then a hand hone can be used for finishing after the tool has been hardened and tempered.

Diagram D shows a single-point cutter for facing from the chuck, the holder consisting of rectangular mild steel bar with a reamed hole for the bit, which is held by a grooved cotter.

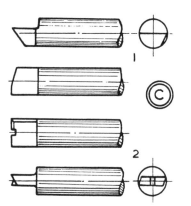

Collet Chucks
(November 1954)

We illustrate here a chart giving the specification for various sizes of standard collets as employed on the best known types of precision lathes. This particular list was compiled by Mr. George Gentry from data supplied by the late Mr. George Adams, and was published in the issue of *The Model Engineer* dated November 29th, 1934, together with further particulars and general information on these chucks. A drawing of a lathe mandrel, showing standard type of draw tube, is also given here.

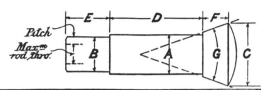

G.A. Sizes	Dimensions						Angle G	Pitch	Max rod thro.
	A	B	C	D	E	F			
L	6 / ·236	5·1 / ·201	10·5 / ·413	17·5 / ·689	7·5 / ·295	5·5 / ·217	40°	36 T.P.I.	2·7 / ·106
	6·5 / ·256	5·5 / ·217	10·5 / ·413	17·5 / ·689	7·5 / ·295	5·5 / ·217	40°	40 T.P.I.	3 / ·315
A	8 / ·315	7 / ·276	13 / ·512	19·5 / ·768	9 / ·354	5·5 / ·217	40°	·625³⁄ₙ	4 / ·157
B short	10 / ·394	10 / ·394	14 / ·551	23 / ·906	11 / ·433	8 / ·315	30°	83³⁄ₙ	6 / ·236
Long	10 / ·394	9·2 / ·362	14 / ·551	52 / 2·047	16 / ·630	5·5 / ·217	40°	1³⁄ₙ	5·5 / ·217
D	12·5 / ·492	11·5 / ·453	18·5 / ·728	68 / 2·677	18 / ·709	8 / ·315	40°	1³⁄ₙ	7·5 / ·295
C short	15 / ·591	13 / ·512	21·5 / ·846	32 / 1·260	14 / ·551	8 / ·315	40°	1³⁄ₙ	9 / ·354
CL long	15 / ·591	14 / ·551	22 / ·866	55 / 2·165	20 / ·787	9 / ·354	40°	1³⁄ₙ	10 / ·394
F	20 / ·787	20 / ·787	28 / 1·102	68·5 / 2·697	22 / ·866	10 / ·394	40°	165³⁄ₙ	15 / ·591
L	$\frac{15}{64}+2$	$\frac{13}{64}-2$	$\frac{13}{32}+7$	$\frac{11}{16}+2$	$\frac{19}{64}-2$	$\frac{7}{32}-2$		36 TPI	$\frac{7}{64}-3$
	$\frac{1}{4}+6$	$\frac{7}{32}-2$	$\frac{13}{32}+7$	$\frac{11}{16}+2$	$\frac{19}{64}-2$	$\frac{7}{32}-2$		40 TPI	$\frac{1}{8}-7$
A	$\frac{5}{16}+3$	$\frac{9}{32}-5$	$\frac{1}{2}+12$	$\frac{49}{64}+2$	$\frac{23}{64}-5$	$\frac{7}{32}-2$		40·64·	$\frac{5}{32}+1$
B	$\frac{25}{64}+3$	$\frac{25}{64}+3$	$\frac{35}{64}+4$	$\frac{29}{32}$	$\frac{7}{16}-4$	$\frac{5}{16}+3$		30·6·	$\frac{15}{64}+2$
	$\frac{25}{64}+3$	$\frac{23}{64}+3$	$\frac{35}{64}+4$	$2\frac{3}{64}$	$\frac{5}{8}+5$	$\frac{7}{32}-2$		25·4·	$\frac{7}{32}-2$
D	$\frac{1}{2}-8$	$\frac{29}{64}$	$\frac{47}{64}-6$	$2\frac{43}{64}+5$	$\frac{45}{64}+6$	$\frac{5}{16}+3$		25·4·	$\frac{19}{64}-2$
C	$\frac{19}{32}-3$	$\frac{1}{2}+12$	$\frac{27}{32}+2$	$1\frac{17}{64}-6$	$\frac{35}{64}+4$	$\frac{5}{16}+3$		25·4·	$\frac{23}{64}-5$
CL	$\frac{19}{32}-3$	$\frac{35}{64}+4$	$\frac{55}{64}+7$	$2\frac{11}{64}-7$	$\frac{25}{64}+6$	$\frac{23}{64}-5$		25·4·	$\frac{25}{64}+3$
F	$\frac{25}{32}+6$	$\frac{25}{32}+6$	$1\frac{7}{64}-7$	$\frac{45}{64}-6$	$\frac{55}{64}+7$	$\frac{25}{64}+3$		15·59·	$\frac{19}{32}-3$

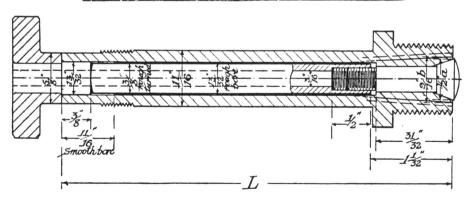

Second Operation Set-Ups

'Geometer' (January 1957)

A sound lathe-work principle is to machine as much as possible of a component at a single chucking in order to preserve alignment between faces and concentricity on diameters and to save time in resetting.

Many chucks do not hold really truly, particularly after a period of use, and there are components whose slenderness or fragility renders their rechucking a problem. Often, of course, a second set-up is inevitable and consideration must then be given to ensuring truth, avoiding distortion, and performing the work with the minimum of trouble.

A diameter, bore, or face on material gripped and machined in the chuck is obviously true until the material is moved, so that any such feature employed for alignment will result in a component being true on a second set-up.

Stub mandrels, as at A, machined from material held in the chuck, provide for the true setting up of bushes, sleeves, small wheels and pulleys, previously finished in the bore either by accurate boring in the lathe or drilling and reaming. Friction drive is sufficient for light cuts, and a mandrel can be turned with a slight taper, or a taper produced by a Swiss file and/or abrasive cloth. Pushing a component on by hand is sufficient and, in some cases, a smear of oil is

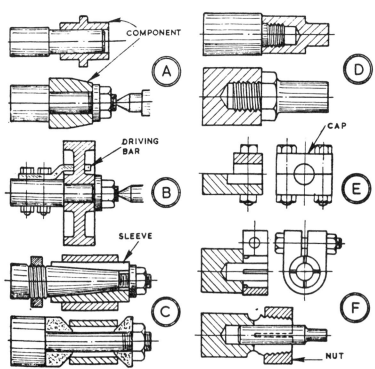

advisable to prevent seizing. If the component is tight a clamp or protected-jaw pliers may be needed for removal.

Using a nut and washer, a component can be gripped on a mandrel; and when overhang is considerable support can be given from the tailstock. Mandrels may also be run between centres—but, naturally, more time is needed for making them. For ordinary stub mandrels scraps and off-cuts of most common materials can be used—mild steel, brass, aluminium alloy; and they can be given a reference dot mark to No 1 jaw for rechucking when necessary—or set up in an independent chuck.

A problem may arise when a large diameter must be turned with the component on a mandrel, since a friction grip, or even a mounting with a nut on the end of the mandrel, will not ensure a slip-free drive. In the case of wheels or pulleys with spokes or holes, a solution is to employ a driving bar bolted to the mandrel and shaped and "set" as required to pass between spokes or through a hole. The mandrel should be partly finished, the bar fitted, then removed while the locating diameter and face are machined. Again support from the tailstock may be necessary in use, as at B.

On more elaborate mandrels to run between centres an expanding sleeve or opposed cones may be used in the bores of components, as at C—the cone type somewhat wanting in accuracy. For the expanding sleeve the mandrel is tapered and the sleeve slit lengthwise to be displaced by a nut. A second nut at the large end is advisable when the mandrel taper is slight—to free the sleeve by screwing back against it.

Provided with threads externally or internally stub mandrels in the chuck afford means of setting up screwed components, as at D, for operations on the outer ends—turning, facing, threading, etc. To ensure truth, threads on the mandrels should be screwcut or cut with dies or taps from the tailstock.

Spindle-type components or those with shanks for location can be set up in various sorts of clamping or contracting mandrels or collets. A simple and effective type can be made from flat stock, as at E, by bolting on a cap and setting in an independent chuck for drilling and boring—the cap then being eased on the joint face for a grip to be obtained on the shank of the component.

Collets to contract and hold components can be as at F. For the clamping type the stub mandrel is bored, turned, and a small undercut made at the shoulder. Without removing from the chuck the end is slit lengthwise with a fine saw. For closing, a clamp as shown is better than a collar with a screw. The type with a nut can have a taper thread by not running the die on fully, while the nut can be undersize from not passing the tap right through.

Boring Recesses
H.K. (November 1935)

It frequently happens that a recess, such as that indicated at a in the accompanying sketch, has to be cut in a bore, to a

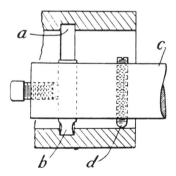

definite depth, by means of a tool *b* which is similar to a square-thread tool and is supported in a boring bar *c*.

Gauging the depth of such a recess is usually difficult during machining, but the provision of a stop on the boring bar in the form of the screw *d* enables the recess to be cut accurately to the desired depth.

The tool projects from the boring bar while the stop *d* projects to a lesser extent. If the difference in projection equals the radial depth of the recess, the tool will be cutting to the desired depth, when its movement is limited by contact of the stop with the bore of the work.

Lathe Toolposts

J.H. Davis (October 1969)

The $4\frac{1}{2}$ in. Barnes lathe has a T slot for the toolpost and after considerable use the projecting parts on which it clamps become badly worn and tend to be pulled through the tool supporting ring. In an endeavour to spread the load I made a T piece as per sketch and then turned off the end of toolpost as shown to $\frac{1}{2}$ in. dia. $\times \frac{5}{16}$ in. long and tapped a hole in the end $\frac{3}{8}$ in. BSF and made a screw to hold the parts together. This screw is done up tight with just enough clearance to allow the toolpost to swing round freely.

The T slot for the toolpost on the

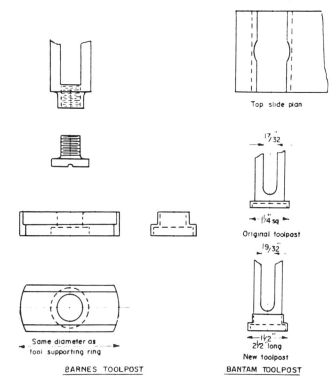

Top slide plan

$^{17}/_{32}$

Original toolpost
$1\frac{1}{4}$ sq

$^{19}/_{32}$

New toolpost
$1\frac{1}{2}$
$2\frac{1}{2}$ long

BANTAM TOOLPOST

Same diameter as tool supporting ring

BARNES TOOLPOST

24

Colchester "Bantam" lathe is of a different design but I felt it would be worth adopting a similar idea here. Viewed from above a hole is bored through into the T slot, this is to locate a post for the modern quick change tool holders and is also, I think, a point of further weakness due partly to the fact that the base that goes in the T slot is only a flat plate $1\frac{1}{2}$ in. sq. × $\frac{1}{4}$ in. thick in which the end of the toolpost sits.

Having decided to make this new piece, I thought I would make a new post as well because the one sent with the lathe was a bit dumpy and only had $\frac{5}{8}$ in. bearing for the clamping screw. In the new one the tapped hole for the screw is nearly $1\frac{1}{2}$ in. long.

Anyone owning a Colchester "Bantam" lathe may be interested in the following idea.

The recommendations on the thread cutting index plate are for English threads per inch, either $3\frac{1}{2}$ to 24 or from 14 to 80, using gears on the quadrant plate 35-120-30 or 21 into 120 and 100 into 60 respectively. For my own general use and not wishing to be continually changing the quadrant gears, I find the former too coarse and the latter too fine.

So by using gears 35-100-60 on the quadrant I can read from the equivalent positions on the index plate threads from 7 to 48.

Of course I have these listed for easy reference on a card near the lathe.

A High Speed Turning Hint
W.J.S. (July 1935)

When turning brass at high speeds, the small cuttings fly off the work with some force, and it is always a good plan to use an eye shield. Apart from protecting the eyes, there is another point to consider, and that is the small cuttings flying in all directions take a good deal of time in clearing up. In order to confine the cuttings in a small space on the lathe bed, the writer uses a shield, as shown at A, in the illustration. The shield is easily made from a piece of thin sheet metal, and is supported in the tool holder on top of the tool. Make the shield about three inches wide, and bend it so that it stands above the work a distance of one inch.

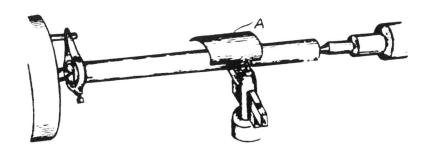

A guard to arrest flying chips from lathe tool.

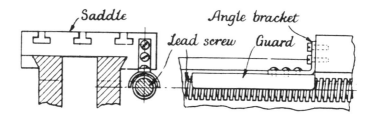

Saddle   Angle bracket   Lead screw   Guard

A Simple Lead Screw Chip Guard

E.L. Pott (September 1935)

Having purchased a 3-in. Zyto lathe, I decided to make a lead screw chip guard, as there was not one fitted. I obtained a piece of steel gas pipe about 4-ins. long, internal diameter a little larger than the diameter of lead screw, sawed it down in half lengthwise, and then riveted a piece of steel strip on to it, bent at right angles. I next screwed the end of the strip to the lathe saddle and adjusted the guard so that it just travelled above the lead screw. This fitting is well worth making, because a lead screw soon gets worn if allowed to collect steel swarf, etc., and new lead screws are rather an expensive item.

Clasp Nut Engagement Stop

Martin Cleeve (July 1955)

Whilst I cannot speak for all M.L.7 lathes, I found that mine, at least, suffered from the fault of being without a definite stop to determine the degree of engagement of the half-nuts with the leadscrew, it being found that when the lever was depressed to effect engagement, there was nothing to prevent the half-nuts gripping the screw with such force that a very considerable torque was required to effect the rotation of the leadscrew — it was found almost impossible to move it when attempting to do so by hand turning a 40-tooth change wheel mounted thereon.

To say the very least, it was considered that the arrangement was open to improvement and, whilst it could, of course, have very little effect on the driving motor, it might well upset a screw-cutting session, and might even be a means of leading a novice astray, apart from placing a considerable and unnecessary extra load on a screw-cutting gear train.

The leadscrew fitted to the M.L.7 has a thread of Acme form which, without going into precise details, means that the threads have sloping sides. One result of this is that when cutting a screw, it will be essential that the half-nuts engage to exactly the same depth at each closing, if the anticipated results are to be obtained.

Perhaps the principle of this can best be illustrated by taking an extreme case, for the purpose of which it may be assumed that a cut has just been taken with the half-nuts engaged 100 per cent. and a following cut made with only a 50 per cent. engagement; that is, with the nut engaging "half way up" the leadscrew thread; this would bring about a serious lag in the position of the saddle and tool, one possible result of which might be, for example, that, had ten thou. been added for the second (lagging) cut, the tool would only rub at the trailing end, whilst the operator, being perhaps a novice, or one not familiar with the theory behind his actions, would possibly withdraw the tool, add another ten thou., and take another cut, this time with full engagement of the half-nuts — the tool would now be taking *double* the depth of the first cut, whilst the machine would probably register its protest by making extra loud "gear noises" indicative of undue strain, and the thread form would be spoilt.

Damage from swarf

Again, where there is no limit (other than binding on the leadscrew) to the depth of engagement of the half-nuts, the depth of engagement could be more easily upset by the accidental entry of a bit of swarf

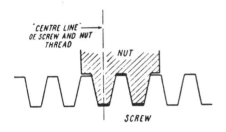

A 100% ENGAGEMENT - NO LAG

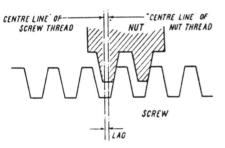

B PARTIAL ENGAGEMENT. NUT "LAGS" ACCORDING TO DEPTH OF ENGAGEMENT

Fig. 1 *Diagram illustrating effect of imperfect or irregular engagement of half-nut(s) with leadscrew of Acme form, and showing how a screwcutting operation could be upset as described in the text.*

or metal chip, which could easily prevent the re-engagement of the half-nuts to the original depth; moreover, lack of a definite stop results in the foreign matter being well rammed into the softer metal of the half-nut to act as an extra source of wear to the leadscrew, until detected and hooked out with a scriber point during routine overhaul and inspection.

In addition to the foregoing, the discerning user will be interested in one further aspect to the question: as has been mentioned, with full engagement of the half-nuts, there is a very considerable load on the leadscrew which diminishes with an easement of the half-nut lever. Thus, unless the half-nut lever is operated with exactly the same force at each successive engagement, the varying loads placed upon the screw-cutting gear train will introduce varying degrees of distortion in that train, and in the spigots holding the tumbler reverse gears and other idlers, also in the leadscrew itself, which twists at the driven end before commencing to revolve in the half-nuts. All these factors contribute to a varying degree of lag in the relative position of the screw-cutting tool and the accuracy of the thread being cut.

A simple remedy

With a view to obviating this unpleasant set of potential trouble-making circumstances, and to introduce a measure of reliable consistency to the operation of screw-cutting, it was decided that some sort of depth engagement stop must be fitted to the half-nut mechanism and, after removing the lathe apron and giving the matter a couple of hours consideration, the following method was adopted as being the simplest solution, and one which would not spoil the external appearance of the apron.

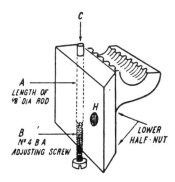

Fig. 2 *Showing where the stop rod (A) is fitted in the lower half-nut. The rod and screw may be placed as near the centre as possible, consistent with not interfering with the ¼ in. B.S.F. hole (H), which will be found to be towards the right side.*

Reference to Fig. 2 will show that a stop-rod has been fitted to the lower clasp-nut, consisting of a suitable length of $\frac{1}{8}$ in. dia. steel rod, A, running, through the slide portion of the nut and rendered adjustable by means of a No. 4 B.A. cheese-head adjusting-screw B, the idea being that when the half-nuts are closed, the upper end, C, of the $\frac{1}{8}$ in. rod, A, meets the corresponding under surface of the upper nut, and thus determines the degree of closure.

Whilst detailed instructions for the carrying out of this simple bit of fitting are obviously not called for, it might be mentioned that about one-third length of thread should be found satisfactory, and a lock-nut may be fitted if desired, although the writer found that, due to a slight difference of pitch in the screw and tap, coupled with the length of the screw, a lock-nut was not necessary.

To remove apron and half-nuts

A note on this has been included for the benefit of those who may not be familiar with the easiest method, which is:

(1) Remove the leadscrew collar, change wheel and Woodruff key.

(2) Remove the right-hand leadscrew bearing bracket from the lathe bed, and slide out the leadscrew to the right. (Put the leadscrew in a safe place, where it will not get damaged or dirty.)

(3) Unscrew the three cap-head screws which go down through the top front of the lathe saddle, and the apron will be freed.

(4) Remove the clasp-nut operating handle.

(5) Remove the screwed pin from the lower half-nut and slide out nut.

Whilst the apron is removed, it would be a good idea to examine and clean the other half-nut and to clean the vee-ways and check the adjustable gib setting, as well as to have a look at the rack traverse gears, to see that they are free from swarf. The writer, by the way, found the screws holding the gear cover box in position were in need of a tighten-up.

Final adjustment

After fitting the stop and re-assembling, it is a simple matter to make the final adjustment.

When the half-nuts are open, the stop adjusting screw is readily accessible at the base of the apron, and should be slackened off until the half-nuts grip the leadscrew, whereupon, by getting the feel by hand twiddling a change gear mounted on the leadscrew in the orthodox position, the stop adjusting-screw should be screwed up by *small* increments and the half-nuts operated until the leadscrew is free to revolve, but without undue backlash in the nuts.

If and when further wear takes place, it will be a matter of a few moments to re-adjust the stop-rod to suit.

Just one more note: when re-fitting the lathe apron to the saddle, it will be found that it is possible for it to deviate slightly from its proper position, which should be such that, when the half-nuts are closed, the leadscrew is not forced towards or away from the lathe. This point should be checked before giving the cap-screws their final tighten.

Simple Tool
R. James (February 1947)

The drawing shows a tool and holder I made and use frequently. The tool is simply a broken Slocombe drill ground to a radius to get a smooth finish. It is very useful, and as it is high-speed tool-steel, it cuts almost anything. I hope it may interest other readers.

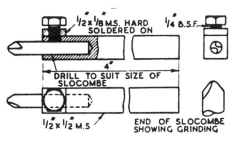

secure the piece of M.S. by one hole, pointing towards chuck. Take out the screw from carrier and run a nut on it, now insert it from the back of M.S. strap in the other hole and screw on the carrier body lightly. Chuck one end of the spindle, now slide up and set over poppet, so that the spindle can slip through the carrier. Adjust carrier screw until spindle is just steadied by the vee and screw, and then lock to strap by means of nut. It may be necessary to use a little packing in places to ensure free running. Lock poppet to bed, lubricate, and turn with light cuts. The above was used on a 4 in. Drummond lathe, but can, no doubt, be adapted for others.

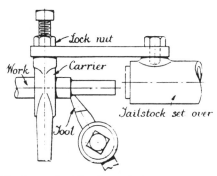

The improvised fixed steady in use.

Improvised Steady
L.G.S. (July 1935)

A simple steady can be made up as described below, when it is required to reduce the ends of fairly long spindles. Select a carrier of about $\frac{3}{4}$ in. capacity, also a piece of M.S., about $3\frac{1}{2}$ in. × 1 in. × $\frac{1}{4}$ in., with a hole at each end, such as is used for holding work to the boring table. Remove locking screw from poppet, and with a set screw of the same thread,

Screwcutting B.A. Threads
J.H. Balleny (July 1955)

I trust that the reproduced chart (see overleaf) may be of interest to many of your readers. You will see that it gives screwcutting trains for B.A. threads from 0 to 12, and has been compiled especially for the M.L.7 lathe. It is, of course, applicable to any lathe with an 8 t.p.i. leadscrew provided that 21, 38 and 46 tooth wheels are available.

B.A. NO.	DRIVER	I ST. STUD		2 ND. STUD		LEAD SCREW	PITCH ERROR INCHES	ERROR PER INCH THREADS
		DRIVEN	DRIVER	DRIVEN	DRIVER			
0	45	40	21	IDLE 50 WHEEL		75	− 0·00002	+ 0·010
1	45	25	21	40	21	70	+ 0·00004	− 0·030
2	20	35	25	40	50	70	− 0·00005	+ 0·042
3	20	60	45	IDLE 40 WHEEL		65	+ 0·00010	− 0·173
4	20	60	25	IDLE 50 WHEEL		40	+ 0·00004	− 0·060
5	20	35	25	55	50	70	− 0·00001	+ 0·020
6	20	60	35	IDLE 45 WHEEL		70	− 0·00010	+ 0·150
7	25	46	20	50	45	65	− 0·00010	+ 0·246
8	20	50	20	45	46	60	+ 0·00014	− 0·474
9	20	50	20	IDLE 55 WHEEL		65	− 0·00002	+0·060
10	35	40	21	50	21	70	− 0·00001	+0·100
11	25	46	21	50	30	70	+0·00003	− 0·192
12	20	38	20	50	25	60	− 0·00004	+0·290

Setting Lathe to Turn Parallel
J.H.D. (August 1935)

When turning a job between centres, it is necessary to test it with a micrometer at two positions a fair distance apart, to see if the lathe is turning parallel or not. This hint will save considerable time, and it should be used on every job of this nature, because when resetting the tailstock at different positions on the bed, it will be found that the lathe will not always cut dead parallel. Take a roughing cut along the centre of the job, as shown in sketch, leaving about $\frac{1}{2}$ in. each end; light cuts can now be taken over these two portions, tested with the micrometer, and the tailstock adjusted as desired, until the lathe cuts dead parallel or near enough for the job in hand.

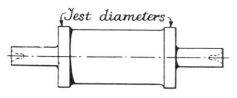

Test diameters

How to Plane Small Gears
'Geometer' (February 1964)

Although small gears can be bought in many sizes, they must sometimes be made at home because a standard one is not right in size, in number of teeth or in material. You may need a steel gear instead of a standard one of brass; or a gear which is to hand may have too few or too many teeth to give the required ratio. And there is the satisfaction which comes of making all the parts of a model or mechanism yourself.

Providing that the gears are of fine pitch, planing with a form tool in the lathe is a practical way of making them, a gear blank being turned to size and mounted with a change gear on a mandrel when the lathe lacks a division plate or other means for indexing. The tool is clamped to the topslide, like a turning tool, but with its profile facing the headstock; and the saddle is used to make cuts, which are taken down to the depth of tooth by the cross-slide. This method cannot be used for large teeth, which must be made on a different set-up with a rotary multiple-toothed cutter or a flycutter.

For planing, you need a tool of the proper size and shape in silver steel, which is first hardened outright and then tempered to the usual dark straw colour at the working edge. The shape of the tool varies with the number of teeth in the gear. To make a tool, you need a pattern gear which has either the same number of teeth or a number which is within a given range. You cannot use a rack as a gauge or pattern to make a form tool to plane a pinion with 12 teeth, or *vice versa*, for the two tooth shapes are entirely different.

Standard involute gear cutters are made in sizes each of which covers a range of teeth. We can choose in these ranges a gear which we can use as a pattern or template to make the tool for planing another gear. Particulars of standard cutters are:

No 1 cuts gears from 135 teeth to a rack, inclusive.
No 2 cuts gears from 55 teeth to 134 teeth, inclusive.
No 3 cuts gears from 35 teeth to 54 teeth, inclusive.
No 4 cuts gears from 26 teeth to 34 teeth, inclusive.
No 5 cuts gears from 21 teeth to 25 teeth, inclusive.
No 6 cuts gears from 17 teeth to 24 teeth, inclusive.
No 7 cuts gears from 14 teeth to 16 teeth, inclusive.
No 8 cuts gears with 12 teeth and 13 teeth.

Now, if we have a pattern gear with 40 teeth, and we need a gear with 50, we can use our gear for the form tool, turning the gear blank to a suitable size. It is the same if we need a gear with 35

teeth, as this, like the other, is in the same range (No 3 cutter). But if we have a gear with 15 teeth (No 7 cutter), we cannot use it as a pattern for a form tool for a gear with 30 teeth (No 4 cutter), as the profile is not suitable.

Diagram A (see overleaf) shows a set-up for planing a gear. A steel mandrel which is held in the chuck has a change gear keyed by a peg and clamped by a nut. At the front end is a bore in which the stock of the centred blank is gripped by pointed screws. This blank is turned with normal tools; and when the gear has been planed, the stock can be chucked and the gear drilled and bored to fit its shaft. The waste material comes in useful for other jobs.

On occasion, a change gear is mounted direct on the stock of the blank, but a mandrel allows for the use of different change gears. Thus, one with 60 teeth can be used with 60, 30, 20, 15 and 12 teeth. One with 80 teeth can be used for gears with 40, 20 and 16 teeth.

Diagrams B and C show the form tool and an index. The index is made in mild steel, with a flat base, a round pillar and a swivelling detent, clamped by a nut at the top. It can be adjusted through the slot in the base to change gears of different size.

The trickiest part of the whole job is, of course, the making of the form tool. To get the profile of a tooth space, you need good eyesight, a magnifying glass or a bench microscope. File a silver steel tool to fit one flank of a tooth. Harden and temper the tool and use it to machine a curve on a light-alloy lap on a mandrel. Prepare the form tool as accurately as possible by filing, and mount it on the vertical slide. Use the lap one way and the other, as at D and E, raising and lowering the tool, as at F, while feeding the lap with grinding compound above a

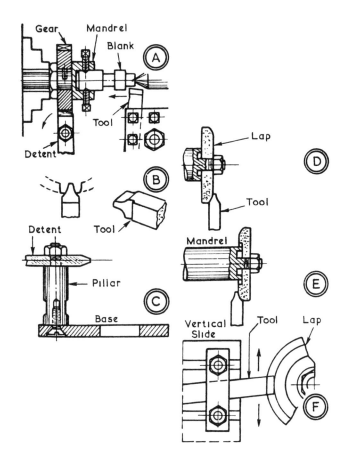

tray on the lathe bed. Lap each side of the form tool until it fits the pattern gear exactly. Then harden and temper it. In this way you get a centralised form, the same each side, so that teeth on your gear are not malformed or falling over.

A Centre-Spacing Punching Tool

Dr. J. Bradbury Winter (May 1927)

It often happens that a series of holes are required in a circle, either on the face of a job or on the outside edge.

To make a circular scratch and cross scratches and centre punch the points of intersection is inaccurate and slow.

For such jobs I have a piece of $\frac{3}{8}$-in. square steel, about 4 ins. long, with a hole, about No. 45, near one end, and in this hole a piece of steel wire $\frac{5}{8}$ in. long

Small centre punch mounted for use in the lathe.

is a good sliding fit. The wire is formed into a centre punch point at one end, and hardened. (*Vide* sketch.)

Put this tool in the slide-rest, and with the help of the division plate and light taps of a hammer, the required marks are made accurately and quickly, and without the necessity for any lines.

In order to make the hole in the square steel a good fit, or in any similar cases where a nice sliding fit is required, I file five facets on a piece of the same steel wire for an inch or so, thereby making it into a reamer or parallel broach. When this has been passed through a slightly smaller hole, the original wire will be a perfect fit.

Boring Bar Attachment

A.J. Dew (April 1924)

One of the tools we have to use on the lathe is the boring bar, and when it comes to cutting a slot in the bar and fitting cutters for various jobs, the time and labour becomes a consideration.

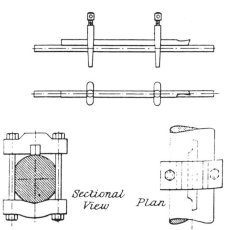

Convenient way of mounting light cutters on boring bars.

The attachment I am describing was designed for facing the sides of the crankshaft bearings in the main castings of small power gas engines, and the type of cutter used has done me a good turn on lots of jobs.

I have used a cutter of this sort (see sketch) on a bar as small as $\frac{1}{4}$ in., counter-boring a hole in wrought iron big and deep enough to take a $\frac{1}{4}$-in. nut, which needs a socket wrench to turn it, of course.

For a job of this sort the cutter needs grinding away behind the cutting edge so as to clear the hole as it goes in, and in this case the cutter can be rather long and held on to the bar by two lathe carriers in place of the clamp, as shown for the larger bars.

In the event of the cutter not covering a large enough area, a face can be cut in steps, packing the cutter out from the bar each time.

It will be noticed the cutter is double-ended, so as to cut either right or left, and the attachment can be fitted to various size bars.

The clamp is made out of $\frac{5}{8}$-in. square iron, the bolts are 5/16th in., and the cutters are made out of $\frac{1}{4}$ in. square high-speed steel.

Turning and Boring Phosphor Bronze

J.H.D. (September 1935)

It is usually advised to have no top rake on tools, although I prefer just a very little myself. Take the first cut deep enough to get well under the skin, run slow, with the back gear in if necessary; this will be desirable if cast steel tools are used. Do not use too fine a feed for roughing. When skin is removed inside and out, speed up the lathe, but phosphor bronze cannot be cut at the same high

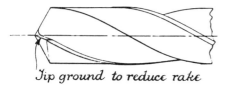

Tip ground to reduce rake

speed as brass. Grind twist drills as per sketch for cutting brass and phosphor bronze, but only for drilling into solid metal: do not use to open cored holes. A flat drill can be used for this purpose, held in the toolpost. High speed steel lathe tools and drills are to be preferred to cast steel.

Query—Form Tool of Complicated Shape

I wish to make a form tool, for use on the lathe, to the shape shown in the accompanying sketch. The exact radius of the portion marked (X) is not important, but I wish the "vees" to be clean and sharply pointed. My difficulty is that I do not see how I am to grind these "vees" on an ordinary bench grinder, which is all the grinding equipment that I have. Your help and suggestions would be much appreciated.

Form tools of complicated shape, such as you require, cannot be ground accurately on an ordinary bench grinder, and would, indeed, present difficulties on almost any type of grinding equipment, if the ordinary flat type of tool is required. These forms may, however, be made fairly easily if a circular type of form tool is used. By this method, the form is turned on the edge of a circular blank of tool steel, in the manner shown in our sketch, the accuracy of the form depending entirely on the skill of the turner.

For the dimensions you require, the blank should be about $1\frac{1}{2}$ in. in diameter,

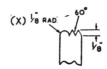

and it may be of soft high-speed steel, high-carbon steel, or even of silver-steel, which is, of course, hardened afterwards.

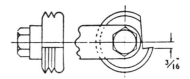

A portion is then ground away, as shown, to provide a cutting edge. In order to obtain sufficient periphery clearance, the cutting face is off-set below the centre of the tool. For a blank of $1\frac{1}{2}$ in. in diameter this amount should be about $\frac{3}{16}$ in. A top rake of about 10 deg. should be used for working on steel, but no top rake is desirable for operation on brass. The tool should be secured to a steel shank with a sturdy bolt.

Curing the "Incurable Chuck"

Dear Sir,—It may interest those of your readers who suffer from the "incurable chuck" of the three-jaw S.C. type, which is too far gone for grinding, etc., to know how I overcame my difficulty in that direction.

I was employed at a firm of electrical engineers as toolmaker, and I had considerable spare time jobs of the repetition type to be done on our old "Hack" lathe (our own name for a bad lot), the chuck of which was hopeless for accurate work. I dismantled said chuck and thoroughly cleaned, etc., and re-assembled less *chuck back*. I obtained a piece of mild steel which was turned accurately between centres and long enough to go right through the chuck, leaving about 1″ extending each end. In the centre of this mandrel, I fitted the chuck securely with its *own jaws* in the usual manner. I then turned and re-recessed the back of the chuck, whilst running between centres in the usual manner for pulleys, etc.

My next move was to clean and fit the chuck back to the lathe nose, then I refaced and lipped it truly to fit the re-paired chuck. As there was ample thickness in the chuck back, this operation was easily performed without fear of weakening. After refitting the chuck to the back and trying a sample of round steel in it, I found, by test indicator, that the chuck was true to about half a thou., which limit was about the same over the entire range of the scroll.

Not so bad for an apparently hopeless job, eh?

(September 1936)　　　　Sid Rowley.

Tightening Adjusting Screws on Cross Slides of Small Lathes

J.A. Butler (November 1936)

It is frequently found that the adjusting gibs to the boring tables and cross slides of small, medium-priced lathes are difficult to keep pressed tightly, and yet freely, against the slides. The screws which hold them in place will loosen under the vibration of cutting.

In my lathe, this had the effect of leaving minute ridges in the work, and of causing cylinder bores, etc., to come out tapered.

The difficulty was overcome by taking out the adjusting screws, cleaning them carefully, and tinning thinly over the threads with soft solder. Once replaced, I found that they very rarely need adjusting.

Cutting Multi-thread Screws

O.S. (October 1936)

Multi-thread screws can be easily cut on a lathe by the following method. A multi-thread screw consists of two elements — the pitch of the thread and the number of separate threads in this pitch. Suppose we want to cut a double-threaded screw with a pitch of 1/12″, then in every 1/12″ there will be two separate threads, and in one inch of the screw there will be 24 threads.

Set up the screw-cutting gear to cut 12 t.p.i. and put in the toolholder a chaser for 24 t.p.i., and cut in the normal way. This will produce a double-threaded screw, each separate thread having a pitch of 12 t.p.i. A three-thread of the same pitch would be cut by using a 36 t.p.i. chaser, and so on.

Query — Knurling Troubles

Can you advise me, please about a trouble I encounter when knurling? I am using a single-wheel knurling tool, and while I am fairly successful (but not always) in obtaining a plain straight or diagonal knurl, I am in trouble when attempting a double diagonal knurl; that is, when using right- and left-handed knurling wheels in succession. The second wheel usually wipes out the first set of knurling completely, or so cuts it up that the appearance is destroyed.

It would appear that you are applying far too much pressure to the second wheel. The surface left by the first wheel is not solid, as it is in the first instance, but consists of a series of ridges, which are fairly easily depressed. The second cut should not, therefore, be taken at the same lathe setting, but the pressure applied gradually until, by inspection, it is found that the cut is complete.

Knurling should be done step by step, with frequent pauses to allow the wheel to cut, but a fairly hard initial pressure should be applied, so that a firm knurl begins to form almost at once. If the initial pressure is too light, the surface tends to break up and become "fluffy."

Plentiful lubrication with soluble oil or lard oil should be given, and the teeth of the wheel cleaned occasionally with a stiff brush.

Twisted Rods

Sir,—With reference to your problem of twisted brass rods.

I have recently completed a Fowler Big Lion and the method I employed was as follows: —

Square brass tube was cut to 1 in. plus, annealed and filled with lead, a bush with a square hole was fitted in the chuck and another in the tailstock. The brass was then placed in the holes and the chuck pulled round the required number of turns, after which the lead was melted out.

Incidentally I worked at Savages, King's Lynn, for a brief period.

(February 1969)   C. Lines

A Chuck for Small Screws

"Ned"

Nothing looks more unsightly in a model than screw ends which, having been found to protrude too far after assembly, have been sawn off and either left in this condition, or roughly trimmed with a file. Quite apart from the matter of appearance, however, such screws are liable, when subsequently withdrawn, to damage their tapped holes by the inevitable burrs which are bound to be left on the screw ends after sawing or filing. If again assembled in the same condition, it will

be found difficult to enter them in the tapped holes, especially if in inaccessible positions, and it is more than likely that they will enter cross-threaded.

From all points of view, therefore, it is important that the screws should be cut to length before assembly, and the ends properly rounded off in the lathe. This, however, is often more easily said than done. A cheese-headed screw may be held in the chuck, though with some risk of marring the head; but a round-headed screw is very difficult, and a countersunk screw almost impossible to hold in this manner. The usual expedient of threading two nuts on the screw and locking them to allow of holding the screw in the chuck is clumsy and tedious, besides being inapplicable to very short screws.

The device shown in Figs. 1 and 2 is a simple solution to this problem. It is easily made, and will hold any round, countersunk, cheese or hexagon headed screw within its capacity, down to a very

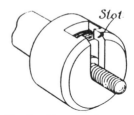

Fig. 1 *Chuck with screw in position.*

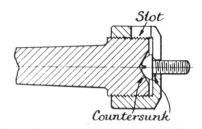

Fig. 2 *Section of chuck, showing how screw is centred.*

short length. The body or shank may be made with a taper stub to fit the mandrel socket or screwed to fit the mandrel nose; alternatively, it may be made parallel, and held in the three-jaw chuck, though this is not recommended, owing to its liability to run out of truth. It is screwed externally with a fine thread, and the end faced off squarely and countersunk in the centre. The cap is screwed internally to fit the nose, and drilled centrally a clearance fit for the screw to be held, the inside of the hole being countersunk slightly. In order to facilitate inserting and removing the screw, a slot is cut from the hole to the edge of cap, and suitably widened on the outside diameter to allow the largest screw head to pass. The countersunk centres of the body and cap will automatically centre the screw, and it will be found that several sizes of screws can be held quite truly, but it is a simple matter to make a cap to suit any special size of screw to be operated upon.

Overcoming the Deficiencies of Inaccurate Machine Tools
Edgar T. Westbury (September 1936)

The old saying that "a bad workman always finds fault with his tools," may contain a great deal of truth, but like most old sayings, is often abused by being turned inside out. In other words, it is definitely wrong to say that anyone who finds fault with his tools is a bad workman; on the contrary, it is only by finding and fully recognising the faults in tools that one can ever hope to make the best use of them. There are faults in the very best of machine tools, as indeed, in any work of men's hands, however excellent, and the application of delicate tests will show how far from perfect the most careful attempt to produce a straight line, a circle, a plane surface or a definite angle, really is. That being so, one might be led to take up the attitude that, since nothing we can make will possibly be accurate, it is futile to ever try and make it so; but from a practical point of view, the engineer accepts the inevitable, and his ideas of accuracy are based upon the limits of error which can be detected by his measuring instruments. In normal engineering practice, these are considerably smaller than are allowable in the work to be produced, and thus there is no difficulty in measuring with reasonable accuracy; production of good work therefore depends upon intelligent and skilful manipulation of the available tool equipment.

Methods of obtaining accuracy

In producing a piece of work to a given standard of accuracy, two diametrically opposite methods may be employed. First, the work may be cut or formed by tools having no inherent principles of accuracy in themselves, such as a hammer and chisel, or by forging methods, and carefully checked or measured as the work proceeds, until the desired shape and dimension is reached. Second, a machine tool may be used, in which generating or copying principles are employed for the purpose of cutting or forming the work. Success, or relative accuracy of the resultant work, depends entirely, in the first case, upon the manipulative skill of the operator, and in the second case, upon the accuracy of the machine tool employed. Classic examples of the two distinct methods are, first, Sir Joseph Whitworth's surface plates, and second, a steel ball or roller as used in bearings. Both these exemplify very close limits of accuracy produced by widely diverse methods. The engineers of a past decade favoured the first method, mainly through necessity, because accurate machine tools were not available; but modern engineering has become more and more competitive, with the result that manipulative skill is slow and expensive, and the second method is an economic necessity.

The reason for pointing out such obvious facts in detail is to provide evidence that good work with inadequate or inaccurate equipment is by no means so impossible as many people believe. It will take longer, and require more skill, than in cases where precision tools are available, but to the model engineer whose interest is, or should be, in the work itself, just as much as its completion, this should be no deterrent. Indeed, it can definitely be said that some of the finest examples of model engineering have actually been produced with the very simplest equipment. By way of simple analogy, the amateur photographer who possesses an inexpensive camera will often produce better pictures than one having the most elaborate and up-to-date equipment, because although his scope is possibly very much restricted, the absence of artificial aids will cause him to rely more upon his own skill, and devote more conscientious care to the real essentials. This is not intended to suggest that one should not use precision tools, but it is a fact that some operators are inclined to leave too much to the inherent accuracy of the machine, and grudge the use of skill, or in some cases even ordinary care, in its manipulation. The amateur worker should strive to strike the happy medium between the two extreme methods of operation mentioned above, avoiding either slavish dependence on, or complete independence of the machine.

The ubiquitous lathe

The lathe has been called the father of all machine tools. In the amateur's workshop, it is not only the father, but also the whole family, since it is called upon to deal with practically every kind of machining operation. It is, in fact, the backbone of the entire workshop equipment, and the wise amateur will obtain the best lathe that he can afford. Unfortunately, the great majority of people who indulge in mechanical craft for the love of it are by no means affluent, and their expenditure is very strictly limited by economic necessity. As a result, there are few, if any, amateurs who possess the lathe which represents their ideal, and they are forced to compromise, either by purchasing a second-hand lathe of high-class make, or a cheaper class of lathe. In either case, some sacrifice, or at least risk, in respect of accuracy or capabilities is bound to be entailed.

In defence of the cheap lathe

The faults and limitations of the cheap lathe are always being brought forcibly to our notice, but it is only fair to say that in many cases they are very much exaggerated. One often hears that such and such a lathe cannot be used to bore a cylinder or turn a parallel shaft; but it all depends on how much skill or intelligence the operator is prepared to use, and it is fairly safe to say that at the present time there is not a lathe on the market which is not capable of turning out excellent work, up to the most exacting model engineering standards, in the right hands. The cheap lathe is especially suited to the beginner, since its comparatively simple principles and methods of operation are easy to grasp and promote confidence, while the price makes it available to people to whose resources an expensive hobby would be quite impossible. How many would ever take up model engineering in the first place, if it were necessary to spend, say, £150, in the purchase of a lathe* and its tool equipment? There are many well-known figures in the model engineering world to-day who owe their introduction to mechanical craftsmanship to the facilities and attractions of the cheap lathe, and more than one of these lathes has come to be regarded as a milestone in model engineering progress.

It should be pointed out that cheapness need not be inseparably associated with inaccuracy, because cutting production costs involves the necessity of close study of design, while assembly cost is very much reduced by the use of components machined to close limits of accuracy by modern production machinery. The cheap lathe, however, is almost certain to be lacking in finish, and also in individual attention to fit and adjustment. Both these matters can, however, be considerably improved by the user who is prepared to expend time and trouble to this purpose. Even serious inaccuracies are susceptible to treatment in this way, and very often a few hours spent in fitting and adjustment will be the means of saving many dozens of hours faking inaccurate work.

Correcting machine tool inaccuracy

We are always up against the lathe that simply won't turn parallel, or circular, or true, according to the complaints of its operator. Parallel error is rarely, if ever,

(*A basic lathe of similar type and quality to an ML7 cost about £8.50 in the mid-1930s — Ed.)

completely eradicable from any but the very best precision lathes, because the ability of a lathe to perform rectilinear operations depends upon a copying principle, in which the "templates" or straightedges are its own slides. Any clearance, even the most minute, in the sliding or rotating bearings will result in a potential error, which will vary in magnitude and direction according to the stresses applied to them. Thus a lathe corrected for turning the outside of work overhanging from the chuck, would be incorrect for turning between centres, or internal boring. Deflection under applied load also affects parallel accuracy, and lathes of light construction are liable to distinctly measurable deformation. Permanent deflection is often caused by careless mounting of a lathe on its bench or stand.

Errors which are traceable to misalignment of sliding surfaces can be corrected by refitting slides, or in some lathes, by shifting the headstock, but such work should not be undertaken without at least a fair experience of machine tool fitting.

In turning flat surfaces, errors may arise from inaccuracies, not only in the angle of the cross slide to the headstock bearings, but also in the thrust collars on the mandrel and the fixed bearing faces with which they make contact. This defect is comparatively common in cheap lathes, due to hurried fitting, but is fairly easily rectified by carefully remachining the collars and scraping the high spots on the fixed members.

Circular error is not usually serious, even on the cheapest lathes. It can only be caused by appreciable inaccuracy in both the mandrel and its bearings, or by a very poorly supported mandrel which would whip under very slight provocation. An old and badly worn lathe is more likely to exhibit measurable circular error, but in any case, except when caused by deflection, this defect may be cured by lapping both the mandrel and its bearings, not to each other, but in the former case to a true ring lap, and the latter to a straight and truly circular shaft which fits them neatly, and can be traversed to and fro continuously during the lapping process. This method is, of course, only practicable to parallel bearings; cone bearings cannot be lapped, with any great hope of success, except purely for finishing off and removing the last traces of roughness in newly-fitted bearings. As a means of correcting inaccuracy, lapping of tapered mating surfaces is definitely not to be recommended.

If a lathe will not turn "true" (i.e., concentric), the fault is most likely to lie in the fitting of the chucks and centres, or more commonly, through faulty technique in the method of tackling machining procedure.

The user of the modern lathe, however simple or unpretentious it may be, should always remember that the capabilities of his machine, for accurate work, are far greater than that of the best lathes used by the craftsmen of a few decades ago, even for delicate instrument work. Even the luxury of a slide-rest was comparatively uncommon fifty years ago. The expedients of the old-time craftsman are well worth studying, and no model engineer should consider it beneath his dignity to make use of wooden chucks, cement or solder chucks, or any of the so-called "dodging" methods of the past. The use of the hand rest and hand tools is almost a lost art, but they are by no means to be despised, even for precision work.

Making Screws
'Inchometer' (September 1936)

It may seem that notes about this subject are superfluous now that screws are produced and sold at small cost and in almost any size and shape for general mechanical construction. The kind I am implying are those used for connecting parts together, round head, cheese head, countersunk patterns of screw, threaded along the whole or part of the length of the shank. They are made in quantity, as bolts, nuts, keys, pulleys, line shafting and other general engineering supplies are produced; engineering and instrument making firms buy such articles ready made for their normal requirements. But a home worker, at times, may need to have a screw, or several, which is special and does not conform to any one of the standard sizes or threads. Some model engineers prefer to make everything, including screws, themselves, or are situated in localities out of convenient range of supplies. During my visit to Mr. G. W. Parsons, related in my last article, he showed me a particular square head screw; he requires these regularly in his business, so, when work is slack he makes some himself for stock. This suggested to me that information about how to make a screw might be helpful to the "Kindergarten" of mechanical work. There is advantage; you can select the material from which the screw will be made, decide the dimensions of the head, length of shank and how much of it, if any, is to be plain, and fit the plain part tightly or otherwise in the hole receiving the screw.

Turning the shank

The screw is made from a length of rod, iron, steel, brass, copper, zinc, aluminium, according to the material required. Clamp it in a chuck, leaving sufficient projecting to give the entire length of screw, including the head and a margin for cutting off by a parting tool. With chucked work, always have the minimum amount of projection, the farther away the cutting tool operates the more likely will be vibration and spring. A likely result is unevenness of surface and tapering in of the work towards the chuck. These effects may trouble a beginner, he does not recognise the cause, but attributes it to imperfection in his lathe, he thinks he should have plenty of length projecting for manipulation. Turn the length for the shank, indicated by No. 1; diameter is not necessarily to be that of the finished screw diameter. It will depend upon

whether the screwing die is in new condition or is somewhat worn by use, also the kind of die and the kind of metal being screwed. Soft material, such as brass, copper, wrought iron and very soft steel is liable to swell or squeeze up, under the stress put upon it by the die, particularly if the latter is in worn condition and its cutting edges dull. The shank may bind in the die, and, with a small diameter, twist off, giving you trouble to drill and clear out the piece. Alternatively, the metal will tear as the screwing proceeds and the thread be "ragged," as the term is in workshop parlance. For precaution, therefore, have the shank diameter slightly smaller than the nominal diameter of screw, to allow for swelling of the thread. The amount of

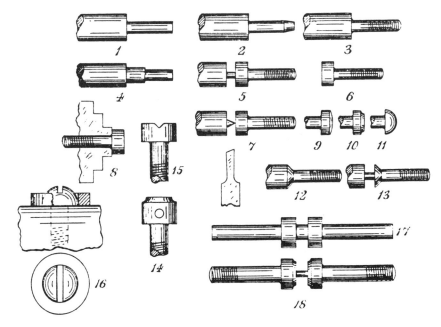

To illustrate making a screw by ordinary tools, showing various patterns of head used in mechanical construction. Numbers are referred to in the text.

under-diameter cannot be stated, you will have to experiment and acquire judgment by experience, it increases with diameter of screw. Supposing that you happen to turn away more than needed, the only result will be an incomplete thread, that is, the top will not be formed. This will not matter, excepting appearance, the core diameter and bulk of thread will not be affected, the screw can still be a good and adequate fit in the nut or hole.

Screwing the shank

If a solid die is used, taper a portion of length as indicated by No. 2, this will assist the die to grip and start the thread. With a two-piece die, taper is not required, grip the die about midway along the shank and screw forward or backward as seems the easier, run the die along the whole length, giving a light preliminary cut. Do not crush in the die with the idea of screwing a "full thread" at one passing, take a series of light cuts along the entire length until a full thread is given. A one-piece die or a screw plate cuts a full thread with one passing. Hence the need of not giving it excessive diameter to remove. With a two-piece die the danger point is when the thread is full, yet is above diameter size. The best course then is to remove the die, file or turn away the extreme top of the thread and apply the die again. My custom is always to use a lubricant when screwing by dies. There is an art in using screw dies: proceed cautiously, never force a die, humour its action. If a portion of the shank is to be plain, as indicated by No. 3, the preferable plan will be to leave it over diameter size, as indicated by No. 4, until the screwing is completed, then turn it down to finished dimensions or fit.

Forming the head

The shank being screwed and turned, the head is formed by turning and parting off from the rod, as indicated by Nos. 5 and 6, the complete screw. Conveniently, use a parting off tool which has a slightly inclined edge, this will leave a "pip" of metal on the rod, indicated by No. 7, and will cut the screw head away clean. Further, the part being cut away is thus conical, stronger than if parallel, and less chance of the tool catching in towards the finish of the operation.

Forms of screw head

The plain cheese head is shown by Nos. 6 and 8, rounded cheese head, No. 9; filleted, No. 10; round, No. 11; countersunk, Nos. 12 and 13, being formed and parted off. Grip the shank in a chuck, No. 8, and turn the head to the shape desired, *before* you cut the slot.

The various shapes can be partly or completely formed as in No. 5, the complete parting off operation being withheld to allow this to be done. No. 14 shows a "tommy head," it is drilled through to take a rod or "tommy bar" instead of being slotted to receive a screw driver blade.

If a small excrescence is left on the head, it will be removed when the slot is cut in. Generally, one would grip the shank in a chuck, as No. 8, the head is then more conveniently accessible for tooling and polishing.

Cutting the slot

This may be done by means of a hacksaw. The shank may be held in the jaws of a vice, or conveniently, especially with a very small screw, in a chuck, and the latter held in the vice. A difficulty is to start the slot, the saw tends to slip about sideways. With a fine three-cornered file, cut a starting groove as No. 15, in which to place the saw blade. As a guide, you might previously have scribed a diametrical line across the head, whilst the screw was in the lathe. A guide to register depth and level of slot is indicated by No. 16, it is a washer or collar of a thickness equal to the distance of the bottom of the slot from the underside of the head. If this is placed, loose, over the head, it will serve as a distance piece and a guide for you to saw level.

Screwing hard steel

For ordinary connection purposes, screws made from soft steel are usual and serve the purpose reasonably well. Occasionally you may require a screw to be hardened and tempered, as would be necessary if it is to serve as a pivot bearing, or as a set screw of more than ordinary quality. Soft steel may be case-hardened, but for best service, high grade steel is required. This may be the kind sold under the name of "silver steel," or that generally known as cast tool steel. The latter is not the alloy kind, now much used for cutting tools, and known as "high speed" and self or air hardening, or by other special terms and names. It is a simple carbon steel nominally soft as supplied to you, that is, it can be filed, drilled, and turned, in that state. But unless it is annealed, this steel is severe upon the cutting edge of a tool. The advisable course is not to work it as received but to reduce its hardness by annealing. Heat the piece to dull redness, then bury it in a substance which will delay the rate of cooling; powdered lime is excellent, a heap of fire grate ashes will serve, or put the piece in a domestic fire at night for it

to become red hot, leave it to cool with the fire until next morning. My custom is to refrain from using a one-piece die for screwing cast tool steel at one passing over, even annealed, if a two-piece die is not available, I prefer to cut the thread by a single point tool, or by a screw chasing tool, until it is nearly formed, then finish to size by the die, so that the latter is not stressed to much extent. My experience in using silver steel is that it should not be annealed but be worked in the state as supplied. A one-piece die may be used to cut the thread with one passing; this material is, therefore, convenient for very small diameter screws; cutting by single point tool or a chaser would be troublesome.

Screwmaking between centres

The home mechanic, perhaps, does not possess a self-centring or other chuck suitable for holding a length of rod; or the screw to be made is of too large diameter or too great a length for available chucking. It can be made between centres of the lathe. If several are required, they can be turned and screwed two at a time as indicated by Nos. 17 and 18, the former shows the roughing out stage, the latter the finished screws ready for being finally separated. By the same method, pins and other turned details may be produced. Put centres in the ends of the rod, and turn the shanks, reversing the rod for the second, and leave enough metal to come off for finishing to size. Part down between the heads to a diameter about equal to that of the shanks. Proceed with screwing and turning as already explained. Finish the heads so far as practicable, leaving enough connecting metal to support the whole, divide by means of a hacksaw and finish by filing and emery cloth in the vice. Rounding and filleting is conveniently done by means of a graver and round-nose hand tool. To turn a fillet commence with a flat bevel, then curve out by the round-nose tool. It is general practice to round the end of the shank of a screw or a pin, and not to have it flat. This imparts a good appearance and facilitates the screw thread engaging with that in a nut, or in a tapped hole.

With a pin, similarly, it assists the end to pass into a hole, particularly if the fit is a close one; also prevents burring when struck by a hammer or forced against by a drift or a punch. If work has been turned between lathe centres, as Nos. 17 and 18, leave the centre holes in the ends for convenience of future turning or adjustment of diameter or shape. This will avoid the necessity of re-centring.

Benchwork

Hints on Filing

"ATLAS" (July 1898)

The choice of a file for a particular job is often looked upon with indifference by the amateur. But the idea that "any file will do," is a wrong idea, and is sometimes very disastrous to economy. New files should always be kept for use upon brass or cast iron, as a blunt file has very little effect on these metals. In the case of cast iron, however, the outside surface or "skin" of the casting should first be removed by chipping, grinding, or some other process, before applying a good file, for this hard "skin" rapidly wears a file out. It is not advisable to use a new file on a very narrow surface, as there is a tendency for the teeth to break. When files lose their cutting power to some extent, and do not cut well on brass or cast iron, they may then be used with good effect on wrought iron and steel. When working on wrought iron or steel, little particles of the metal are apt to get lodged in the teeth of the file. If this happens the bits should at once be removed, or they will cause deep grooves and scratches in the work. It is very annoying when this happens on a surface which is nearly finished, so bear in mind that "prevention is better than cure," and keep your files clean.

Do not throw your files all in a heap on the bench, as one knocking against the other will cause damage. Lay them side by side, or better still, put them in a rack at the back of the bench. Have a handle for every file, and keep every file to its own handle. When putting a handle on a new file, take care to put it on nice and straight, for not only is it more comfortable to use, but good work can be done more easily than when the handle is crooked.

Files are made with different degrees of roughness, and the following are the most useful kinds:- "Rough," "second cut," and "smooth." Where there is a lot of metal to come off it is best and quickest to use a rough file first, and to finish off with a second cut or smooth. The smooth files should not be used to take much metal off or they will soon be worn out, but should only be used for finishing off a surface. If a high finish is required and at the same time there is very little to come off, a "dead-smooth" may be used, but it is very rarely that this file is required. A second-cut file is very useful for filing steel. Files should not be allowed to rub against the hard jaws of the vice, as they will thereby soon be spoilt.

The height of the work to be filed should be somewhere about level with your elbow. Stand with one foot about six inches to the left of the vice, and the other about fifteen inches behind the vice. Hold the handle of the file in the right hand and the other end of the file in the left hand, and work with a firm steady stroke, remembering only to apply pressure during the forward or cutting stroke. Try to feel the position in which the file bears evenly on the surface of the work and endeavour to maintain that position during the whole of the stroke. By filing diagonally in alternate directions, the cutting marks of the file show where it is affecting the surface, and the stroke can be altered accordingly.

File Cleaning
'Inchometer' (June 1964)

We are often recommended to clean a file by rubbing it across the teeth with the end of a piece of brass strip: brass presumably being specified as the least likely material to cause a premature blunting. This is strange, when you consider that files are made to cut steel, including carbon tool steels, some of which are quite hard even in the annealed state — silver steel, for example.

I have a very fine (and favourite) file in constant use for finishing diameters such as may be required to very close limits for ball-race fitting. But the file is so smooth that rubbing brass strip across the teeth will not remove some of the more securely embedded particles, and I have to use mild steel. A convenient size is $\frac{3}{8}$ in. $\times \frac{1}{16}$ in., about 6 in. long, with the end ground flat on the side of a grinding wheel. It will remove every trace of

foreign matter.

My favourite file is now about 20 years old. Apart from giving it the steel-strip treatment, I have wire-brushed it thousands of times, yet it still performs pleasingly. "An uncommonly good file," the sceptics may say . . .

The Art of Drilling Holes
'Inchometer' (September 1935)

To a beginner at mechanical work, drilling a hole may seem to be the easiest and simplest of workshop operations. Regarded merely as pushing a drill through a piece of material and thus producing some sort of a hole, it may be very easy to accomplish. But if the hole is to be circular, accurately to position, straight and in line of position, the operation requires accumulated skill, knowledge of the technics of drills and experience with materials and the kind of machine or other appliance used. There is an art in drilling and boring holes. With each operation practised in mechanical work there is an art, whether drilling, turning, boring, filing, planing, brazing, or any line of mechanical operation; accept it as being a separate art for you to investigate, study and treat with respect. Have I daunted your desires, efforts and intentions by picturing an involved outlook in this intended recreation that you contemplate or have already adopted? A lady friend had purchased a fine concert harp and informed me that she intended to learn to play upon it, as a hobby. Knowing something about harps and harp music, I remarked that it was a difficult instrument — proficiency would need years of study and practice. The lady replied: "I have taken up the harp as a recreation. I do not wish to learn it all at once." Should not this view apply to all recreations and hobbies? Do you want to become a fully fledged top notch experienced mechanic "all at once"? If you will approach your hobby with the idea that it is to serve as a source of enjoyment through learning its technics, apart from being a means of effecting constructions, you will find a continual interest with manipulation alone, and in discovering and dealing with the inherent difficulties.

Winding Small Springs

B.C. Wood (January 1947)

The following method of winding small springs may be of interest to readers. I have used it for a number of years after seeing a description in a handbook— Kempe, I believe—but it does not seem to be generally known.

I. Tension springs. A piece of ebonite or fibre is held in the vice and two sets of holes are drilled. Those on the left serve to tension the wire which is threaded through alternately front and back; those on the right act as "bearings" for nails or

suitable size mandrels held in a hand drill chuck. The end of the wire is poked between the chuck jaws, and the nail is rotated, keeping the coil gently pressed against the ebonite as it is formed, i.e. the hand drill is progressively pushed backwards towards the body.

II. Compression springs. This method is almost uncanny in its action and produced hearty laughter the first time it was tried.

The same piece of ebonite may be used, a small hole for the wire being drilled 1/32 in. away from the edge of the "bearing" hole. The wire is fed through from the far side and into the chuck jaws. The spring is then wound up as before, taking care to keep the coil closely pressed against the ebonite. On releasing pressure, it will be found that the spring will separate its coils automatically.

A spring with internal diameter smaller than the mandrel will be produced if the wire is fed through a nick in the side of the bearing hole instead of through a

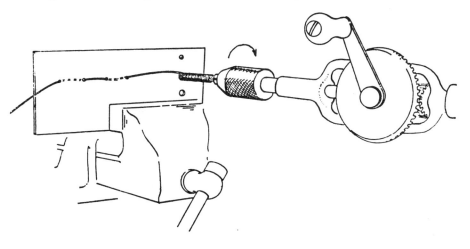

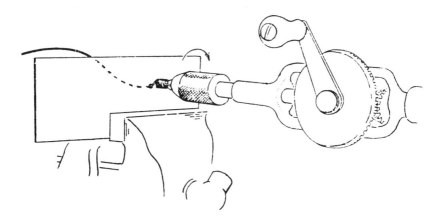

separate hole. In a similar way a more open-spaced coil may be produced if a mandrel larger than finished spring size is used.

The spring ends are finished off "L.B.S.C.-wise" on a fast-running grinding wheel.

Prevention of Noise
E.C.A. (November 1935)

To model-makers whose workshops are located in or near dwelling houses, a simple means of deadening the noise of hammering, etc., is a great relief. There are two methods, which are as follow:

(1) A rubber cushion under each leg of the work-bench; these may be cut from disused solid rubber tyres.

(2) Small boxes of sand or saw-dust applied in the same way. A few inches of sand or saw-dust is poured in each box, on this is laid a board or block upon which the leg rests, and around the leg and block is poured fine dry sand or saw-dust. Not only all noise, but all vibration and shock is prevented. An ordinary anvil, so mounted, may be used in a dwelling house without annoying the occupants.

Small Bends, Sets and Joggles
A.E.U. (July 1955)

The appearance of a model, or indeed any example of engineering work, is much enhanced if all the minor parts show evidence of neat and careful workmanship. Such bent components as shackles, eyes, and chain links in bright mild-steel present certain difficulties in this respect, but it is possible to produce them in such a way as to avoid spoiling the original finish with hammer marks, bruises and burrs.

If one has considerable dexterity with round-nosed pliers, and the work is small enough in section, then all is well, but what about the jobs in $\frac{1}{8}$ in. dia. and above? Bending jigs are needed to make a decent clean job of small rod work. Shackles, for instance, are a tricky job to make neatly without such a jig.

Jigs for shackles, eyes and chain links

The body of the shackle jig is a piece of plate as thick as the inside width of the shackle, with the edge radiused the same as the bottom of the U of the shackle. Three holes must then be drilled and reamered for the pins around which the rod will be bent. Pins A and B must not stand proud of the body more than one diameter of the rod being bent, C must project at least two diameters. As an added refinement to avoid flattening, A and B, *but not C*, can be formed rollers, held by a pin. Pin C should be a loose fit in the jig body. The jig body should be long enough to hold in the vice without interfering with the bending operation.

To form the shackle, the rod is first pulled down over the jig, as in Fig. 1. (It is sometimes necessary to knock the rod down on to the jig with a soft dolly or a drift, the business end being formed to fit the rod section.) Pins A and B are then inserted, and the rod pulled back round B, as in Fig. 2. Pin C is then inserted, and the rod wound around C to form the eye. The surplus rod is best cut off whilst the shackle is still on the jig; the eye can then be knocked down flat on to the jig. If the eye is to be brazed, the rod should be cleaned before the eye is knocked down.

Pin C should be the same size as the hole required in the eye, as the rod

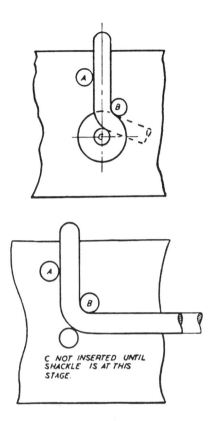

C NOT INSERTED UNTIL
SHACKLE IS AT THIS
STAGE.

Fig. 2

usually winds around C very tightly. Some materials are ductile enough to work cold if the radii are large; most steels, however, work best hot. Mild-steel, for example, works best at bright orange. When working with mild-steel, only that part of the rod requiring to be formed should be heated for best results. The easiest way to achieve this without an oxy-acetylene torch is to heat the rod by whatever means may be available, and then dip into a bucket of water to cool the rod up to the point required, both sides of the part to be formed. It

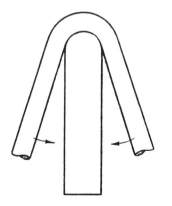

Fig. 1

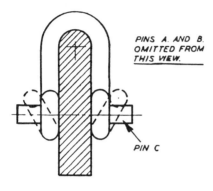

PINS A. AND B.
OMITTED FROM
THIS VIEW.

PIN C

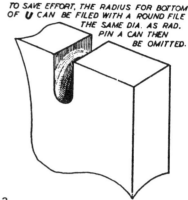

TO SAVE EFFORT, THE RADIUS FOR BOTTOM
OF U CAN BE FILED WITH A ROUND FILE
THE SAME DIA. AS RAD.
PIN A CAN THEN
BE OMITTED.

The finished shackle on jig. Dotted line shows
rod before cutting off surplus

Fig. 3

is best to form one radius at a time.

Eyes are made in the same way as shackles, except that two *A* Pins (one either side of rod) are required. Chain links are made in a similar fashion, the form of the centre plug depending on the chain (see Fig. 4).

Sets and joggles in small details

It is most difficult to set small details without distortion, especially those forming part of a locomotive valve-gear, due mainly to their relatively large cross section, compared to their length, and even when distortion is overcome, there is still the question of maintaining reasonable accuracy. The easiest way to overcome distortion and inaccuracy is to make a simple bending tool to use in the vice; see Figs. 5, 6 and 7. The part to be set or joggled should be supported by a couple of pins in the tool, and the tool should be supported in the jaws of the vice so that the work-piece can be adjusted before the vice grips it. The two halves of the tool should be located, relative to each other by a couple of

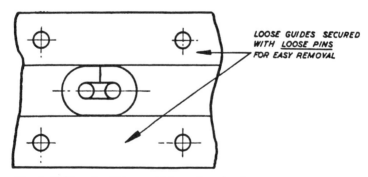

LOOSE GUIDES SECURED
WITH LOOSE PINS
FOR EASY REMOVAL

Fig. 4 *Guides should be as thick as dia. of rod.*

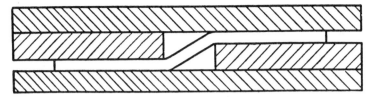

Fig. 5 *Section of typical tool, showing job in place*

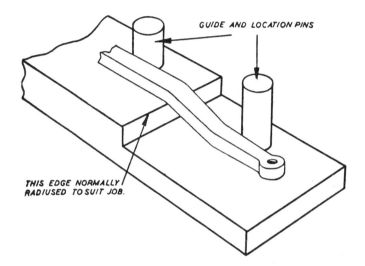

GUIDE AND LOCATION PINS

THIS EDGE NORMALLY
RADIUSED TO SUIT JOB.

Fig. 6 *Half tool with job on completion of joggle.*

PUCKER OR INDENTATION
CAUSED BY TOO SHARP A
CORNER ON DIE BLOCKS

Fig. 7

guide pins (loose fit in tool, holes should be +0.002 to +0.005); the same pins can serve to locate the work-piece.

When using stiff or springy material, an allowance will have to be made for "spring back." But for mild-steel, it is not usually worth bothering with. Most parts will work quite well cold, using the tools shown in the sketches.

Sharp bends in rod with very small corner radii are best formed in bending blocks used in the vice. The blocks are made in one piece and cut apart after drilling. The holes should be drilled with

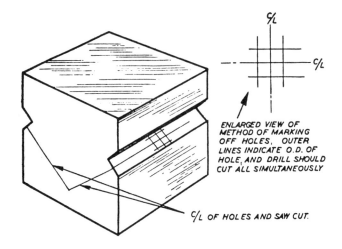

ENLARGED VIEW OF METHOD OF MARKING OFF HOLES, OUTER LINES INDICATE O.D. OF HOLE, AND DRILL SHOULD CUT ALL SIMULTANEOUSLY

C/L OF HOLES AND SAW CUT.

Fig. 8

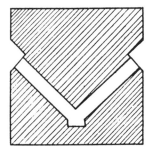

Fig. 9 *Section after drilling.*

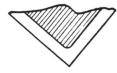

Fig. 10 *Section of male half with corner radius filed.*

a drill of the specified size, without using a pilot hole so that the hole will be slightly oversize (see Figs. 8, 9 and 10).

Adjustable Wire-bending Tool
W.H. Grayling (April 1927)

The sketches show a useful tool which may be used for wire bending, straightening, or cutting. It is designed for use in a vice, and is of simple construction. It is made of steel throughout, shaped as shown, with a dovetail slot down the centre. It is made tee shaped for convenience of gripping in the jaws of a vice.

Two pieces are made to fit, and slide, in the dovetail slot. The end of one is shaped to form a cutting edge, and the other end has two tapped holes to take a locking screw and a shouldered post as shown.

The tee portion of the tool is tapped at intervals all over its surface to take shouldered posts. These posts may be of various sections, as shown in detail, and may be square, triangular, oval, or whatever shape required.

It will now be seen that by means of the slides the posts may be placed in various positions, relative with each

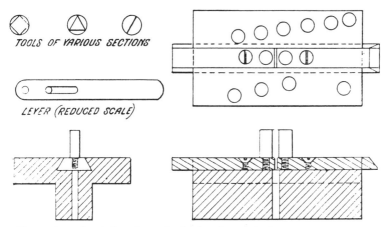

TOOLS OF VARIOUS SECTIONS

LEVER (REDUCED SCALE)

Plan and sectional elevations of wire bending gadget.

other, and almost any complicated bend may be obtained in a simple manner.

By gripping the tool in the vice with the centre hole clear and reversing the slide with the cutting edge towards the centre, and slipping the lever over the posts, the tool is then used as a wire cutter for various purposes.

Winding Helical Springs
N.F.F. (April 1927)

By means of the device shown in the sketch, open or close wound springs can be made with a minimum amount of trouble and danger in the ordinary lathe.

The correct diameter of the mandrel A

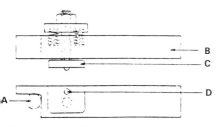

Device for winding springs.

can only be obtained by trial; one made seven-eighths of the inside diameter of the required spring is generally about right.

The device consists of the shank E which is held in the tool-post of the lathe.

The front portion is cut away to rest against the mandrel A; the wire being kept taut by passing it through the spring clamp C between the shank and the pin D, thus preventing it from working out.

When the spring has been wound it should not be cut off until the lathe has been turned back a few times and the coil has expanded to its normal size.

Working Pipes and Tubes
'Geometer' (December 1955)

The important thing to remember when working pipes and tubes is to avoid collapse and splitting. The various methods employed are governed by material, diameters, wall thickness, radii and angles of bends.

When sawing thin-walled tubing, fine-pitch hacksaw blades are essential; by holding the tube in the vice, inserting a

53

close-fitting mandrel or rod and placing packing round the outside distortion can be prevented, as at A. Alternatively, soft clamps can be made from pieces of board, gripped together and a piece of thin cardboard placed between them, these are drilled centrally to the size of the tubing. Large size clamps can be bored in a four-jaw chuck.

Copper and brass pipes of small diameter but relatively thick-walled can be bent easily unless the radius of the bend is very small. For a bend of minimum radius, the material should be annealed, i.e., heated to red and quenched in water. Small steel pipes should be bent at red heat unless the curve is very gradual, when cold bending is possible.

Bending small pipes

A bend of particular radius can be obtained by turning the pipe round a piece of suitable rod and a coil can be made by carrying the pipe the required number of times round the rod. Where there is surplus pipe, it is often best to bend first and cut afterwards.

In bending larger pipes or tubing of thinner section, recognition must be made of the fact that, as at B, the material round the outside of the bend X must stretch and that on the inside Y must compress. If bent unsupported or without means of effecting the stretching and compressing, the tubing will either acquire an oval section or collapse and split at the bend.

Bending larger pipes

To prevent this splitting and collapsing with pipes that are not too large, fill them with lead or white-metal, bend them when

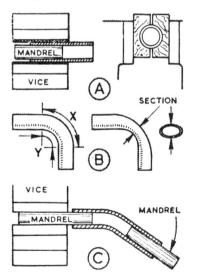

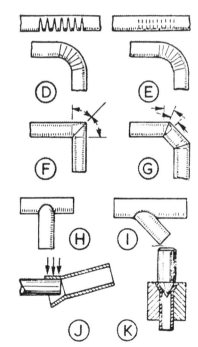

cold and then heat to clear them. Larger pipes can be plugged at one end, filled with sand which is rammed tight, then plugged and bent as required; steel pipes should be heated. The sand must be quite dry to avoid generating steam and the risk of a consequent explosion.

Bending can be performed, as at C, by using two mandrels or rods; one is held in the vice and the other is pulled by hand or by slipping it over another piece of tubing.

Very close smooth bends can be obtained on large pipes by sawing out V-sections almost through the pipe, as at D, then pulling it round to the curvature. The join is then soldered, brazed or welded, according to material and equipment. On this principle, neat bends with wrinkles instead of cuts can be made with pipes that are not too large and a welding torch is available. The set-up can be as at C; the torch flame is swung round and concentrated at various points, as at E, to form each wrinkle, and the bend gradually made.

Obtaining angles

Right-angle and other bends can be fabricated, as at F and G, provided the pipes are one size and each is cut at the same angle — half the angle between them. At F, each pipe is cut at 45 deg.

On a bend incorporating three or more pipes, angles are considered individually. At G, the angle between two pieces is 45 deg. and cuts are made at $22\frac{1}{2}$ deg. T-pieces and branch pipes, as at H and I, can be fabricated by filing out the curvature on the joining piece, applying this to the main pipe, scribing round it, then chain-drilling and filing the hole, finally brazing or welding.

Pipes can be enlarged slightly by tapping with a hammer when on a mandrel, on this principle they can be flared, as at J. The mandrel is held in the vice and the pipe fitted on and rotated while being tapped. When flaring, the mandrel is applied at an angle.

An accurate flare or cone can be produced on a small pipe, as at K. A die is produced from two pieces of steel (as for the soft clamps A) by drilling, then running in a centre drill. The pipe is then gripped and opened with a conical punch.

Mandrel for Cutting Rings from Thin Tubing
N.F.F. (1927)

The sketch shows a mandrel for holding a length of thin tubing whilst being parted into rings.

The mandrel A is made of mild steel and is first turned to the outside diameter of the tubing, and then turned to the inside

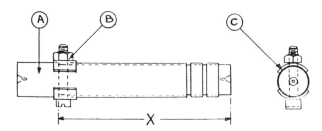

Showing a method of cutting thin tubing on mandrel in the lathe.

diameter as far as distance X.

A hole 3/16th in. diameter is drilled through the mandrel to take the bolt and nut B.

The tubing to be cut into rings is slid over the mandrel and held as shown by the two curved plates C, which are tightened by the nut and bolt.

Adjustable Jig for Drilling Round Stock
D.O. (1935)

For drilling holes dead central through a round bar, the fixture, as shown, forms a useful tool.

The jig comprises, firstly, a base vee block *a* into which are screwed the pillars *b*. These, besides being screwed, should have a plain hole location to ensure pillars being upright and parallel, and should be flatted for points of screws *e*. The top clamping vee *c* carries two liners *d* at a fixed distance to allow top vee to slide down pillars. The liners *d* must have a hole inside to allow clamping screws *e* to lock through on bar.

Central to vee slot in *c* is fixed a liner *f*, into which various size bushes *g* can be fixed to suit size of hole required. Note: liners of bush *f* and *g* should have vee slot to give as long a guide in bush as possible.

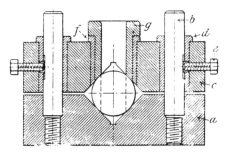

Section of jig used for drilling round stock.

If vee slots are designed correctly, the fixture will cover a good range of work.

The top plate is pushed down on to the work and clamped down with screws *e*, and drilling is then accurately guaranteed.

Handling Small Nuts
C.H.C. (September 1935)

I have found that on the final erection of models there is a difficulty in putting small nuts on the studs or bolts, as there is very often no room to get the thumb and finger holding the nut in the space available. I have found the following dodge very handy. Get a piece of brass wire the same size as stud, screw it both ends, rather slack for nut, and bend one end over at right angles: file off all the threads except two or three, of course, this depends on depth of nut. Screw the nut on wire, chamfered side first, and offer nut up to stud, then with a scriber point or a bit of wire, twiddle the nut off wire on to the stud, and finish up with a box spanner. I always make my box spanners of hard brass tube, as they don't mark the nuts or flange.

Fixing Small Rivets
'Jed' (1955)

To prevent small rivets from turning round after being fixed, use a punch with a triangular point, similar to the counter-sink used by watch-makers.

This makes three triangular nicks in the edge of the hole drilled for the rivet, and when the rivet head is swaged down forms three slight keys, and so effectually prevent if from working loose.

A Simple Marking Gauge
S.R. Smith (December 1935)

This small marking gauge which was

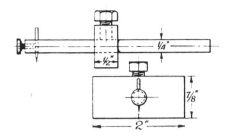

made out of odd pieces of metal will be found useful in marking lines down pieces of metal sheet and strip, or similar work requiring lines parallel to the edge.

The stock was a 2 inch by $\frac{7}{8}'' \times \frac{1}{2}''$ piece of mild steel, drilled for the 4″ length of $\frac{1}{4}''$ silver steel for the gauge rod, with a $\frac{1}{4}''$ Whit. locking screw. The scriber is 1/16″ silver steel hardened and tempered, held in place by a 7 BA. knurled screw.

Toolmaker's Cramps

'L.B.S.C.' (February 1927)

If you don't possess any toolmaker's

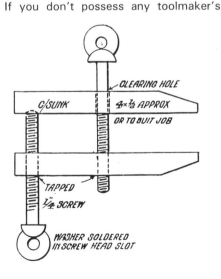

cramps, remedy that omission right away. You can concoct a quite respectable pair of gadgets from 4-in. lengths of $\frac{1}{2}$-in. square steel bar with a couple of long $\frac{1}{4}$-in. steel Whitworth screws in each, as sketch. Your time will be repaid a hundredfold by the ease with which you can clip various bits on to the frames, etc., such as link yokes, guide bar brackets, step and footplate angles and the like. You can shift the parts about to the correct position, and they "stay put" while you drill bolt and rivet holes.

Gear Wheel Repairs

T.G. Wishart (December 1955)

At some time or another, many readers will have had the misfortune of having one or two broken teeth in a gear wheel and have to set about making a repair. The old method of drilling and tapping holes in the root of the tooth, screwing in pegs, and then filling in the spaces with welding is not to be recommended.

For one thing, the welding-rod does not take kindly to the cast-iron; it makes the metal excessively hard and the tooth is difficult to file up to shape. Very often the welding parts company with the parent metal and the tooth slackens, owing to the excessive heat generated in the welding. I have, on many occasions, had to repair these breaks, and the following is the method I invariably employ.

How it is done

The broken teeth are cleared away to at least 1/10 in. or more, below the root of

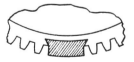

The broken portion of the wheel-blanked out.

57

the teeth according to the amount of metal in the wheel, and dovetailed at the ends, with not too much angle. A piece of mild steel is cut to size and fitted, a light tap-in fit, and then brazed, preferably with Sifbronze.

The whole wheel should first be well preheated all over before brazing and care should be taken to see that the brass flows right through the join. Allow to cool slowly, when the piece can be cleaned up to the existing contour.

The new teeth can then be marked off and either machine cut, if facilities are available, or drilled and sawn out and filed up by hand to template. There is nothing difficult in the job and, if reasonable care is taken, the repair will be every bit as strong as it was before and the join will be practically invisible. If the job is worth doing at all, it is worth doing well.

Chisels from Needle Files

D.S. (October 1935)

Many hundreds of needle files must be broken or worn out every day of the week, yet no one seems to have thought of a way to utilize the marvellously hardened and tempered steel, which is generally thrown into the dust-bin or junk box. I have a fatal tendency for breaking these files, so I looked about for a way to stop the waste.

I ground up the stem and part of the blade, to form small chisels of different sizes and shapes. These chisels are wonderfully hard wearing if used in the proper manner, and require little sharpening, being very hard.

Vee Supports

'Geometer' (August 1963)

The purpose of V-blocks is to support round stock and components by the diameter, for marking-off and testing on a surface plate and for drilling on a drilling machine. The blocks are usually machined and ground in twos, or in batches which can be divided by two, so that each pair of blocks has identical dimensions and angles. This ensures accuracy in use.

By turning a shaft or component in V-blocks, as if it were in journal bearings, the centre on a plain end can be found with a scribing block, and the length can be tested for wobble with a surface gauge or clock indicator.

With the same method of support on a drilling machine, a cross hole can be drilled at right-angles to the axis of a shaft. If care is taken in aligning the drill by eye, the cross hole is also near enough to centre to take a split pin or a taper pin.

These examples are standard practice. Exceptions which are always cropping up for the general engineer reveal disadvantages in the basic methods.

To hold V-blocks securely on a surface plate is a problem when there is no easy way of clamping them. But they must be held firmly, for movement can introduce error and make nonsense of the operation. This is noticed when you are working with a long shaft which overhangs the surface plate.

The low height of standard V-blocks is another draw-back when a component has a flange. To clear it, the blocks have to be raised on parallel packing pieces — which, again, are liable to move.

These and similar problems can be solved for many components with a V support jig as shown at A. It can be made from angle iron, setscrews and nuts in suitable sizes. It is ideal for testing long things such as lathe countershafts and the axle shafts of cars, and for cutting cylinders of lawn mowers and large diameters like hubs and brake drums on axle shafts.

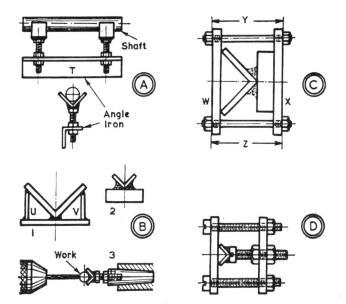

In overhauling a dynamo or electric motor, the armature can be placed in the Vs while the mica is undercut between the commutator segments. To make a firm mounting, grip the angle iron base in the vice by the vertical flange at T. The horizontal flange is drilled for the supports to be set at the required spacing. Pointers or indicators can be bolted or clamped to it. The Vs are brazed or welded to the heads of the setscrews.

Diagram B shows other V supports from angle material in various sizes. The large one (1) for use on a drilling machine is made with a steel base and side struts U and V—brazed or welded for rigidity. The small one (2) is a cheap substitute for standard V-blocks for many purposes. For light work it can be in brass and soft soldered. The V-centre (3) for the lathe tailstock aligns work to a drill in the chuck. Usually holes are more accurately located like this than when they are made with the work in V-blocks on a drilling machine.

In making these supports, the Vs should be set with their faces equally each side of a line which is perpendicular to the base or passes through the centre of the screw. Diagrams C and D illustrate both.

You begin by facing the pieces on their ends in the independent chuck. Then each is placed, V upwards on a flat surface, so that the angles can be compared with a protractor. If you find a difference, you file carefully along the edge of one flange, until the protractor shows the same each side. Then you clamp each V to its base or to its screw, as shown, using flat steel and long studs or screws.

To maintain the setting without heavy tightening, which is not advisable, cut a shallow groove along the top of the base or across the head of an unslotted screw, to receive the sharp edge of the V. In tightening, square up by making dimensions Y and Z equal—and the work is ready for soldering, brazing or welding, according to its size and your heating equipment.

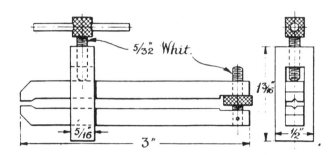

Vice to Set Small Studs

J.H.D. (November 1935)

The sketch shows a small vice I made many years ago for setting small studs in model engines. The two jaw bars were made from $\frac{1}{4}$ in. square silver steel, slightly bent over at one end to form jaws, small vees being filed lengthwise in these to grip the studs. To use, the stud is put between the jaws, and these are clamped on the plain part between the threads by means of the collar and screw provided, the knurled adjusting nut at the other end allowing for various sizes of studs.

Cultivating Caliper Accuracy

W.N. Gardner (February 1927)

The use of calipers needs much practice to ensure good results. The engineer must accustom himself to the use of these tools and cultivate a delicacy of touch in

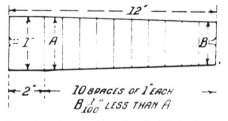

Test piece for acquiring the "feel" of calipers.

order to use them to the best advantage. Mistakes are often caused by beginners having the calipers too tight on the work so that they have to be forced over it; the error so caused amounts to several thousands of an inch. It should always be remembered that the lighter the calipers touch the work the more accurate is the measurement recorded. It is possible, also, to get incorrect results by failing to see that the calipers are being held "square" with the work, also it is essential that the points or ends of the calipers should come "fair" together when closed; that is, the ends parallel with each other and square with the legs themselves.

If the calipers are set so that you can just feel them pass over a cylindrical piece of work, and then hold a piece of thin tissue paper against the side of the work and again try the caliper over both, you will soon learn to note a variation of 1/1,000th in. in size as thin tissue paper, such as cigarette paper, may ordinarily be called 1/1,000th in. thick.

Experience in calipering may also be attained by taking a piece of steel about 1 in. in diameter and 12 ins. long, centring it, and turning 10 ins. carefully so that one end will be 1/100th in. larger than the other, then marking ten lines 1 in. apart on the piece with a sharp-pointed tool. The diameter of the piece will now vary 1/1,000th in. at each line, and by trying the calipers in the various divisions, one may familiarise oneself with any variation that may occur between 1/1,000th in. and 1/100th in. Mechanics have been known to detect a variation of 1/20,000th in. in the size of two cylindrical pieces with a pair of ordinary spring calipers. Others could feel scarcely any difference between two pieces varying by as much as 1/100th in. Of course, such a lack of touch denotes a total unfitness for other than the coarsest work. Finally, let it be remembered that accuracy in this matter can only be cultivated by practice.

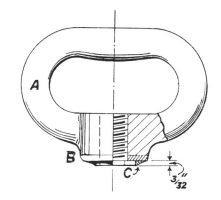

Fig. 1

Wood Lathe Bow Nuts

H.H. Nicholls (July 1964)

The rest and tailstock of a wood-turning lathe were generally clamped in place by "bow nuts" working on long studs projecting from the rest and tailstock castings, through the space between the ways of the bed, and bearing upon two bridge pieces.

A friend asked me to find him such a lathe cheaply, and I obtained one, from which, among other parts, one of the bow nuts was missing. From enquiries in the engineering supply trade I discovered that these nuts were no longer sold. I therefore had to make one.

Having found that the nut A in the illustration was $\frac{5}{8}$ in. Whitworth size, I got a $\frac{5}{8}$ in. Whitworth hexagon head screw, threaded to the underside of the head, and turned the head down to a thickness of only $\frac{3}{32}$ in. Then I cut the threaded part off to finish $\frac{3}{32}$ in. above the boss at the back, and cut a disc of cardboard $\frac{3}{32}$ in. thick to go under the head B. I greased the thread well, screwed all tight, and faired round the hexagon head with putty (C Fig. 1).

When the putty was hard I applied a

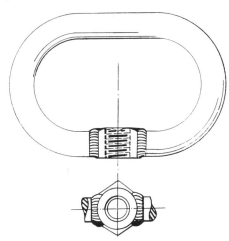

Fig. 2

coat of glossy black paint. I sent the work to Dick Simmonds and Co. of Erith, Kent, and received a perfect casting in iron.

The casting was held on an angle plate by two bolts through the bow part, the boss was drilled out and faced flat, and then the work was put in the bench vice and tapped $\frac{5}{8}$ in. Whitworth. The original nut used as a pattern was, of course,

61

unharmed. I removed the screw and cardboard washer *B* and cleaned and painted both nuts to match the lathe.

I wondered if I might, after all, have been able to buy such a nut somewhere. Then I saw a cement-gun machine belonging to a big firm of contractors. They wanted bow nuts to fasten the door of the cement-grout vessel which fed the gun and had been compelled to make a pair by taking oval chain-coupling links and welding them to $\frac{5}{8}$ in. Whitworth nuts — strong enough but certainly a rough-looking piece of work that would not do on a good lathe (Fig. 2).

Sharpening Small Twist Drills

L. Brown (August 1954)

I am aware that there has been a considerable amount of discussion relating to the sharpening of twist drills, and the somewhat involved geometrical formulae associated therewith. I trust this will not prevent the publication of details of a more down-to-earth solution of this ever-present difficulty experienced by many users of drills. Personally, I have found it impossible to attain the necessary skill accurately to repoint and sharpen drills free-hand, more especially the smaller sizes under $\frac{1}{8}$ in., so that they cut freely and form holes reasonably accurate to size.

These are, of course, the sizes that are not covered by the several drill grinding jigs at present available, some of them at considerable expense.

I have been using my device for some two years with entire satisfaction; formerly I was compelled to admit to failure when required to perform on a small diameter drill.

My device consists essentially of a small vice in which the drill is gripped whilst the two cutting edges are formed

The special vice, with small drill in position.

by honing on an oilstone.

The material required is mild-steel or cast-iron, approx. $1\frac{1}{4}$ in. × 2 in. section, in a length of $2\frac{1}{4}$ in., this to be faced up accurately to the form and dimensions of sketch.

Particular accuracy is required in forming the 118 deg. inclusive angle, and in forming the two small "V" grooves at 90 deg. to base and exactly bisecting the apex angle.

The block is drilled, say $\frac{3}{8}$ in. diameter, lengthways, for twin clamping bolts, it is then sawn into the two vice elements, the sawn faces being accurately machined.

The clamping bolts are a press-fit into one of the vice jaws, or cross pinned, the other having the holes reamed to a sliding fit on the bolts.

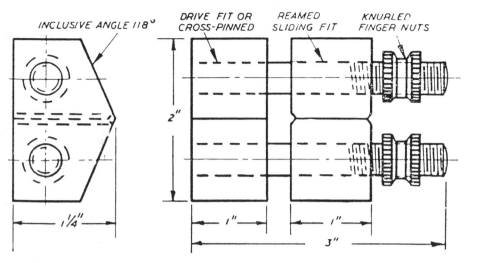

INCLUSIVE ANGLE 118°

DRIVE FIT OR
CROSS-PINNED

REAMED
SLIDING FIT

KNURLED
FINGER NUTS

2"

1¼"

1"

1"

3"

Suitably knurled nuts for the finger tightening of the jaws are required. The exact size and threading of these bolts can be as convenient; $\frac{3}{8}$ in. B.S.F. is suggested.

The sliding jaw has the ''V'' grooves in which the drill is located, and as stated these must be very accurately formed, clean cut at 90 deg. to the base and exactly cutting the apex angle 118 deg. inclusive.

This sliding jaw, if the job is reasonably accurately formed, is reversible, so that either of the two ''V'' grooves can be brought into operation. One groove, it is suggested, should be small enough to enable the smallest drill used to be clamped, and the other to take say $\frac{1}{16}$ in. to $\frac{1}{8}$ in. diameter.

Now as to the manner of using the device; arrange the drill in the groove, lightly clamped, with the point protruding only just enough to allow for the formation of a new point, in order to minimise the amount of honing required.

The only other operation required is to align the centre of one flute of the drill point with the line of the apex of the device, and slightly to rotate the drill anti-clockwise by finger pressure, or with small gripping pliers.

The amount of this offset determines the backing-off angle of the cutting edges, and should be confined to the minimum that will enable the drill to cut freely. This will very quickly be found by a few trials.

For the very small sizes, a good glass will be necessary, or at least a help.

The clamping screws are now tightened, and one face rubbed on the stone until a straight-edge or rule will pass over the surface without obstruction from the drill point, the other face is then dealt with in the same way.

It is particularly noted that both edges are formed on the drill at the one setting thus ensuring correct angle of point, and exactly equal length of the two cutting edges—perhaps the two most essential features of drill pointing. You also have a definite control of the backing-off or relief of the cutting edges.

Of course, you have a flat backing-off; this will, no doubt, horrify the purist and the experts, who can produce the above features free-hand with the addition of a perfectly formed conical point. The fact, however, remains that for all practical purposes of the amateur or model engineer, drills with flat reliefs will cut at least as well and as accurately as those supplied by the makers of drills.

In the very small sizes, drills have always had this flat relief. All I can suggest is that a careful trial is carried out.

I am satisfied from my experience that this device will give extreme satisfaction to anyone who has had any difficulty with drill pointing, but only provided the tool is made accurately in the features emphasised, and care is taken with the setting in the "V".

I have made large models with grooves to take up to $\frac{1}{2}$-in. drills, and have used these in conjunction with an angle-shaped fence or guide fixed parallel to the side face of a grinding wheel. The drill is set in the "V" groove in the same manner as described above, but projecting sufficiently to cover the gap between the guide fence and the wheel. One angle face of the tool is held against the fence and the drill point traversed against the wheel until grinding stops; the other face is then presented to the grinding wheel, and results in a perfectly angled point, with exactly equal cutting edges and with a controllable angle of relief. I am unable to detect any difference in the cutting properties or the accuracy of even large diameter drills ground in this way, as compared with the normal. The chief value, however, is in connection with the smaller drills, which are not otherwise catered for. It should be remembered that all other cutting tools except twist drills have always had a flat relief as accepted practice, including the old spade-pointed drills, "D" bits, and spot-facers, Slocomb centre drills, etc.

My conclusion is that it is only where maximum length of life between grindings is necessary that the conical point is required and shows any practical advantage. With this tool to assist me in the pointing and sharpening business, I am not really concerned with obtaining the maximum possible cutting life between grindings. In any event, it is a pleasant little item to make up, and the cost is practically confined to the time and effort expended.

Beyond the few general constructional suggestions given, together with the sketch and photograph, no further details should be necessary.

A refinement is a short length of compression spring over one of the clamping bolts, to give a spring operated opening motion to the jaws. A recess must be counter-bored in the fixed jaw to receive the spring when clamps are fully tightened.

Drilling Hexagonal Holes
T.W. Tew-Cragg (September 1955)

The operation of drilling hexagonal holes can be accomplished on a bench drilling machine. The principle is to rotate a pentagon-formed drill in the chuck of the driller, and it is guided through a hexagon form directly into the work below, this being clamped to a base that is free to slide horizontally in any direction yet not to rotate.

To design the tools it is first required to know the distance across the flats of the hexagon bolt head; the distance to opposite corners is the product of the distance across the flats × 1.154, which is the diameter of the circumscribing circle of the hexagon.

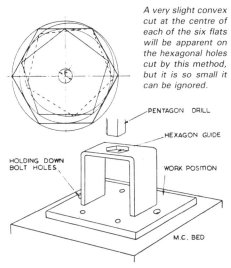

A very slight convex cut at the centre of each of the six flats will be apparent on the hexagonal holes cut by this method, but it is so small it can be ignored.

PENTAGON DRILL

HEXAGON GUIDE

HOLDING DOWN
BOLT HOLES

WORK POSITION

M.C. BED

Now for the drill. The pentagon form has a circumscribing diameter equal (minus running fit allowances) to the width across the hexagon flats and further, the length of one side of the pentagon is equal to the radius of the circumscribing circle of the hexagon. So the drill may be marked out and machined on a suitable steel rod.

The necessary "float" of the work clamp is obtained as follows: the holding-down-bolt holes have a minimum radius of the radius of the bolts used, plus the difference of the radii of the circumscribing circle of the hexagon and that of the pentagon.

Query — Holes in Thin Sheet Metal

Can you tell me please, how I may put a number of closely spaced holes, $\frac{1}{4}$ in. in diameter, through a sheet of No. 28 gauge tin plate. I have tried drilling these, but the holes are becoming out of round, and the edges are tearing badly. I have also tried a hammer and hollow punch, but the holes are almost as bad as those which I drilled.

It is extremely difficult to drill clean holes through thin sheet metal by ordinary methods, but it is possible to do so by clamping the sheet between two pieces of thicker metal, and drilling through the whole assembly together.

In your case, however, we feel that the following method would be simpler and more satisfactory. Clamp an odd piece of flat mild-steel, at least $\frac{1}{4}$ in. in thickness, to the drilling table of your drill. Now drill a $\frac{1}{4}$ in. hole through this, and leave the piece of metal still attached to the drilling table. The $\frac{1}{4}$ drill should now be removed from the chuck, the shank-end ground off square, and reinserted into the chuck with the shank end downwards, i.e., with the chuck gripping the fluted portion of the drill. We have now, in effect, a punch and die accurately located, and clean holes may be punched through the sheet metal; using a sharp downward movement of the drill quill. The drill is, of course, not revolving (see sketch).

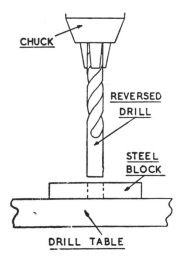

CHUCK

REVERSED
DRILL

STEEL
BLOCK

DRILL TABLE

By this system, holes up to about $\frac{1}{2}$ in. in diameter may be obtained. The method is also extremely useful for making clean holes through such things as cardboard, and in paper gaskets.

Square-ending a Drilled Hole
Nathan Sharpe (January 1924)

It occasionally happens that, for some reason or another, a blind hole is required to have a flat bottom instead of the hollow cone as left by the ordinary drill. A method which can be successfully adopted where only one or two holes require such correction is to take a piece of silver steel of diameter equal to that of the hole, and file away half the thickness at the end, leaving a somewhat hooked lip as shown in Fig. 1. The half-diameter remaining must now be slightly backed off, taking care that the edge is kept straight, and at a *very slight* deviation from the true perpendicular to the axis. On hardening and tempering this to

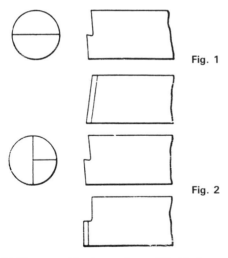

Fig. 1

Fig. 2

Making a tool for bottoming a drilled hole.

straw, it can be fed gently into the hole, when it will remove the cone portion, and leave the bottom of the hole nearly flat, really a little higher in the centre. For some purposes, such as valve seats, this is all to the good, and in most cases it is too slight to be of importance. If, however, a dead-flat bottom is desired, all that is necessary is to finish the drill end *quite* square across, and then remove half the cutting edge altogether to allow for cutting clearance (Fig. 2).

Straightedge and Surface Plate
'Geometer' (August 1963)

A good steel rule is often a substitute for a standard straightedge, but there are times when it is not long enough to reach the whole length of a surface, or diagonally across it when a full proof of flatness is needed.

To prove a large surface would appear to be a tough problem in the lack of proper workshop equipment. Yet it is possible for any engineer to do it by first principles when he knows the trick.

I was reminded of it recently when a friend mentioned that he suspected warping on the cylinder of his car, as he had fitted two gaskets in as many weeks. He wanted to know if it would be possible for him to prove the surface on the next occasion without a long straightedge and a large surface plate.

My suggestion was that he should employ the old principle on which laminated contour gauges are made today. These gauges comprise a number of thin plates, all of the same length. The gauge is pressed to a surface, and the plates take the same curvature on one side and the opposite curvature on the other. When you turn the gauge over, two curvatures of the same sort are brought together and you see any error from straightness doubled.

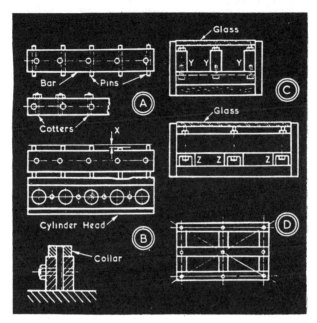

A straightedge to work like this can be made in the workshop as at *A*. You can use it for testing large work, proving standard straightedges and surface plates, testing for wear on lathe beds. In fact, it is a sort of master tool with which an inhabitant of the back-of-beyond can obtain precision.

The back is a piece of rectangular bright mild steel bar, stiff enough to resist bending when it is used as a beam. It is drilled through the depth for parallel steel pins, here five in number, although you can use as many as you need. To hold them, grub screws can be fitted from the side, or the bar can be drilled right through for cotters, as shown.

Cotters are usually better as they can be tightened without the risk of the pins moving in the bar. They can be from small bolts which should be in place when the bar is drilled for the pins. The centres are marked and punched so that the pairs of holes cross at about half their diameters. After the drilling, the cotters are finished by turning the heads from the bolts.

Pins of silver steel rod will give years of service when they have been hardened and tempered at the ends. The material has the advantage over other rod of being reliably accurate to size, so that a shakefree fit is obtained in holes which have been truly drilled or reamed. Good quality mild steel is an acceptable next best, and the pins can be casehardened. Their lengths should be $\frac{3}{8}$ in. to $\frac{1}{2}$ in. more than the depth of the bar to allow reasonable projection top and bottom.

To bring all pins to the same length, as an essential condition for the tool to fulfil its purpose, they should be put in turn

67

into one hole in the bar with a hardened collar on top, and filed. After they have been hardened, they can be carefully lapped in the same way. A micrometer or calipers can be used to check them.

To test the straightness of a face, the two extreme end pins are fixed by their cotters with equal projections from the bar. Then the tool is placed on the face, and the intermediate pins are pushed down and fixed in their turn. If there is a low spot under a pin, its upper end is down to the same extent, as at X diagram B. This error is doubled when the bar is turned over, and so it can be easily checked with a feeler gauge. My friend could thus easily discover any fault with his cylinder head.

Diagrams C and D show how the grid for supporting a large glass surface plate can be made and trued by the same principle. The grid consists of parallel bars YYY bolted to channel sections ZZZ, the bars having adjusting screws in the top for levelling. The whole is enclosed in a wood box.

Query — Scraping Planed Plates
L.K.M. (Wembley)

Q. — I am making a number of small engineer's surface plates. I have machined these ready for scraping, but I do not possess a master surface plate to scrape them to. I understand it is possible to generate a dead flat surface by scraping three plates together, i.e., No. 1 to 2, to 3 to 1 and so on; is this correct? Also, is there any method I could use to check the accuracy of these when finished?

A. — *If you scrape three planed plates to each other, and are assured that while 1 fits 2 and 1 fits 3, 2 fits 3 also, you need no further test; they must all be flat within the limits you care to scrape them. It is, of course, a lot of work, and*

it is best if you take, say, No. 1, as the initial master plate, test that first all ways with a known true straight edge, and then with two known true straight edges placed parallel with each other, first one way across and then at 90° to that way. If No. 1 answers to this, scrape No. 2 to it, working on both. Then No. 3 to No. 1 and finally if after No. 3 fits No. 2 and there is no appreciable error between 1 and 2, and 1 and 3, showing the flatness of all three as a practical proposition, cannot be gainsaid. The closer together in all cases the bearing spots appear, the nearer you are to average flatness. (July 1935)

Non-slip Tap Wrench
W.E. Briley (July 1964)

While my tap wrench has a range from zero to $\frac{3}{8}$ in. it grips the tap firmly on all four sides, whereas wrenches on the market grip only on two opposite corners. The commercial tools also have a nasty habit of slipping round, especially when the handle at one end is used as an adjusting screw.

Besides being a useful tool, the wrench gives the maker plenty of practice at fitting. The main body is cut from a 10 in. length of $1\frac{1}{2}$ in. × $\frac{3}{8}$ in. bright mild steel, and the small angle blocks are made from $\frac{3}{8}$ in. ground gauge, which may be hardened by being heated to cherry red and quenched in oil. The adjusting screw may be made from silver steel and hardened.

Our first operation is to cut the 0.95 in. square hole in the centre of the $1\frac{1}{2}$ in. × $\frac{3}{8}$ in. bar as shown in Fig. 1. It is essential that the hole should be accurate. The small angle blocks all have to be a nice sliding fit inside the square hole. If the work has been done correctly, moving one block in the square will cause the other three to move round in the same

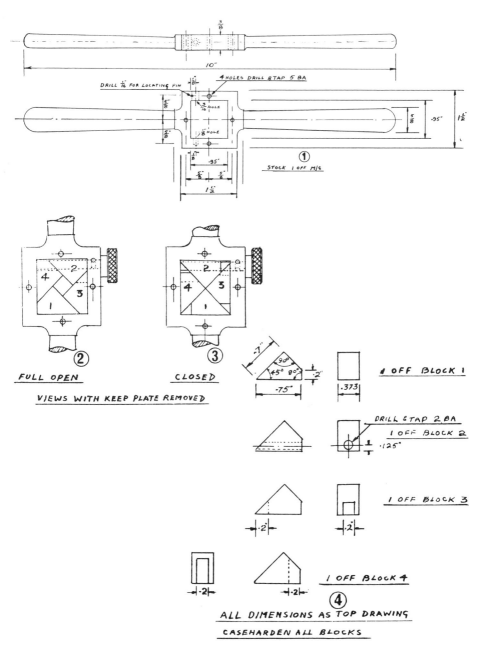

$\frac{3}{8}$

10"

DRILL $\frac{1}{16}$ FOR LOCATING PIN

4 HOLES DRILL & TAP 5 BA

$\frac{3}{16}$ HOLE

$\frac{1}{8}$ HOLE

$\frac{5}{8}$

$\frac{5}{8}$

$\frac{1}{8}$

·95"

·95"

$\frac{5}{8}$

$\frac{5}{8}$

$1\frac{1}{2}$

$1\frac{1}{2}$

(1)

STOCK 1 OFF M/C

FULL OPEN

CLOSED

VIEWS WITH KEEP PLATE REMOVED

(2)

(3)

·7"

90°

45°

80°

2"

·75"

·373

1 OFF BLOCK 1

DRILL & TAP 2 BA

1 OFF BLOCK 2

$\frac{1}{4}$

·125"

1 OFF BLOCK 3

·2"

·2"

1 OFF BLOCK 4

·2"

·2"

(4)

ALL DIMENSIONS AS TOP DRAWING

CASEHARDEN ALL BLOCKS

69

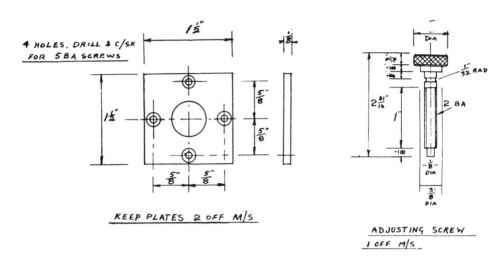

4 HOLES, DRILL & C/SK FOR 5 BA SCREWS

KEEP PLATES 2 OFF M/S

ADJUSTING SCREW
1 OFF M/S

direction. To position the adjusting screw we use a $\frac{1}{16}$ in. pin. The pin engages with a $\frac{1}{32}$ in. rad groove turned under the head in line with the hole drilled for it. It is kept in position by the side plates, or keep plates.

If we drill the $\frac{1}{8}$ in. hole right through the stock (Fig. 1) instead of forming a blind hole, the adjusting screw will then be modified to include a longer $\frac{1}{8}$ in. dia. tail so that two locknuts can be fitted, thus saving ourselves the need of drilling a $\frac{1}{16}$ in. hole and turning the tiny groove.

To Save Broken Taps

C.V. Bavin (January 1947)

Get a piece of mild-steel strip or brass, approximately $\frac{3}{32}$ in., or $\frac{1}{8}$ in. by $\frac{1}{4}$ in. about $1\frac{1}{4}$ in. long, make a square hole in the middle of it to fit the square end of tap and fix strip to tap with a touch of

solder, and use it as a wrench.

I have had a set of $\frac{1}{16}$-in. Whit. taps so fitted some years without breakage, and now fit a similar gadget to all small taps up to $\frac{5}{32}$ in., making the strip of a size proportionate to the tap. The advantages seem to be that each tap has its wrench in readiness, and the leverage is more proportionate to the size of the tap.

Simple Tap Wrench

Sir,—As a toolmaker I feel that the tap wrench (page 470, July 1) is unduly complicated for its purpose. The drawing is of a simpler tap wrench much used by fitters. My own wrench, which has been in use for ten years, is not hardened and shows no sign of wear.

A wrench made to the sizes shown will take taps from 2 BA to $\frac{1}{2}$ in. o.d. For larger sizes the dimensions can be altered

70

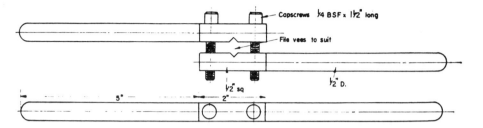

Capscrews ¼ BSF x 1½" long

File vees to suit

½" sq   ½" D.

5"   2"

to suit. The largest wrench which I have made measures 2 ft across and will take taps of up to 1 in. dia. Providing that the V locations are filed with reasonable accuracy, the tool will grip the tap tightly. There is, of course, no possibility of its working loose or slipping.

(December 1964)   D.R. Collier

Tap Grinding and Binding
B.P. (October 1935)

The greatest mistake in grinding and relieving a tap is to relieve it too much. This causes the tap to lock itself into the job. The reason is obvious. Assuming that it cuts keenly, the cuttings curl up in the flutes, but having been relieved too much, on the backward freeing movement, the wedge-like taper of the relieving merely rolls the cuttings back into their original position and jambs the tap. A tap should cut both ways, therefore relieve as lightly as possible.

Lubricants for Tapping

Dear Sir, — With reference to the query of A.L. (Ripon), as to tapping with fine B.A. taps, may I suggest that he uses, as a lubricant, cellulose thinners or methylated spirit. By applying a spot of either of the above in the hole, and dipping the tap in a container, he will find that he will have no trouble, even in stainless-steels. Also, the tap will be clean and unchoked, and

the hole will be dry and easily emptied of swarf.

I use the above method in my work every day, and have not broken a tap in months, provided it is put in squarely.

Try it for removing a locked tap, especially with cellulose thinners!

Cast-iron should be tapped from below if possible, thus clearing by gravity.

(1955)   R.D. Bishop

Some Causes of Taps Breaking
W.J.S. (July 1935)

Perhaps the most common cause of a tap breaking is the forcing of it through a hole which has not been drilled to the correct size. This particularly applies when the job is steel, although it is quite a simple matter to meet with a breakage in the softer metals when the hole has been drilled too small.

Another important item is that of lubrication, and many a tap could have been saved if a little oil had been used.

At first it would not appear that a badly fitting tap wrench could be responsible for a breakage, but this is quite a common cause. The wrench should always be a good fit on the tap in order to keep the turning movement steady and constant.

When tapping steel, it is always a good plan to follow the taper tap with the intermediate one at short intervals, and then finish with the plug tap. In the event of a tap breaking off close to the face of the work, the writer finds that a little muriatic acid, if poured on the tap, will tend to ease it, so that the work of removing it with the hammer and small punch is quicker and less tedious.

Cross-drilling Shafts in Vice

To do cross-drilling in the vice with a top drill-guide, the idea seen in the figure is useful. The guide-plate is made very slightly wider than the shaft diameter, and is split with a saw from each side. This gives a certain degree of flexibility and makes sure that the shaft and plate will be gripped with equal firmness. It also allows for small variations in the size of nominally similar shafts, pins, bolts, etc.

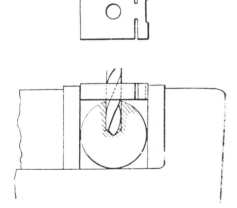

Hacksaw and Scratch Brush Hints
E.C. Chorley (November 1935)

One often wishes to saw out a radius, around which a hack-saw blade of ordinary width will not go, and no other kind of saw is available. If a flexible back blade is cut down in width with a sharp pair of shears, much smaller radii can be sawn. Leave about an inch at each end of the blade the full width, tapering the cut down to the new width. Cut down in a series of narrow strips; the hardened, toothed edge of the blade may crack if too much is taken off at one cut. No softening is required if a flexible blade is used.

The writer has used blades cut down in this manner to $\frac{3}{16}$ in. wide. Care must be taken in use, as the blades are, of course, more fragile.

If the ends of the wires in a steel-wire scratchbrush are occasionally given a light touch on the grinding-wheel, the efficiency of this useful tool will be greatly increased. One keeps other tools sharp, so why not the scratch brush?

A bunch of short pieces of piano-wire pinched into the end of a piece of tube, paint brush fashion, makes a most useful little scratchbrush for use in confined places.

Uses for Powdered Graphite
G.E. Coupland (October 1936)

Keep a small tin of this handy. In any work where fine brass screws have to be inserted into hard wood, there is always the risk of twisting off the top portion of the screw when tightening up, even though a suitable hole may have first been drilled in the wood. The remedy is to lubricate the screw. Oil is no good for this purpose. If anything, it makes the screw still harder to get in. Dip the end of screw in powdered graphite; it will take up a small quantity between its threads, and having drilled a suitable hole (about half the diameter of the screw) it will be found to go in quite easily and can be driven home, and the wood nipped up tightly without any fear of screw breaking.

Before I adopted this plan I spoiled several pieces of fine wood work through screws breaking in. Steel screws can, of course, be similarly treated and their insertion will be greatly facilitated.

If you have a drawer that sticks, rub powdered graphite on the runners, and it will then go smoothly. In all cases where wood rubs on wood or on metal, graphite is the lubricant to use. It is marvellously effective and lasts indefinitely.

Drilling Laminations
J. Kirk (December 1935)

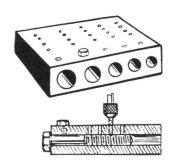

In drilling transformer stampings or similar sets of metal strips, where the holes must correspond exactly, the best way is to clamp them together in a pack. I found it very difficult to hold them close enough to the hole being drilled until I adopted the method shown in sketch (bottom right on this page). An ordinary clamp is used, with a hole drilled through the jaw to act as a jig, a step being first filed on the sloping rib of the jaw, so that the drill starts truly. The moving jaw of the clamp is protected by a piece of wood or ebonite packing.

A Handy Drilling Jig for Joint Pins, Round Bars, etc.
H. Bland (October 1936)

Sometimes it is very difficult to accurately drill through a joint pin bolt, etc. I have found this jig a very useful tool; it can be made from a piece of cast iron or brass and machined all over, or preferably, it is best made from a stock piece of bar steel; the holes are bored and drilled as shown in the accompanying sketch, and afterwards hardened.

The holes bored for holding the work should be of various sizes to take a range of pins or rods. The drilled holes on the top should be of a size which you generally use in your workshop, all of which must be of a definite distance from the end to facilitate measuring the correct position to drill the work to take the pin.

The near hole should be tapped to take a screw for holding the work while being drilled.

The sizes of holes and their relative position in relation to the ends of jig may be engraved or stamped near each hole.

Removing Broken Taps and Drills from Castings

Dear Sir,—I have recently discovered a novel method of removing broken taps

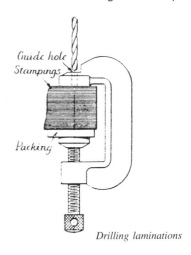

Drilling laminations

and drills from castings, etc., which may interest your readers. A small amount of metal is built up on the submerged tap or drill with the oxy-acetylene blow-pipe, and, while still hot, is turned out with the aid of a spot of oil and pliers quite easily. The job, which is usually a greater mass of metal, remaining at a comparatively low temperature, while the tap heats up quickly and takes the added metal without adhering to the job. Many of your readers may not possess an oxy-acetylene outfit, but most garages do, and will oblige, I have found, for a few pence, if approached tactfully.

(December 1936)					H. Cave

A Simple Hole-chamfering Tool
W.M.H. (November 1935)

This tool, by means of which drilled holes may be chamfered or cleared of burrs, has proved itself most useful.

A piece of 5/8ths diam. cast steel rod 10 ins. long is bent to shape shown in sketch. One end is turned upwards, and a wooden or bakelite handle affixed thereto, permitting same to revolve freely. This rotation may be secured either by leaving a small diametered stalk on rod, riveting the end over when knob is in place, or else by drilling and tapping

a small hole in end of rod and passing a screw through the knob.

To fashion the cutting edges, the rod should first be flattened at two points desired, then filed or ground to shape indicated in the small inset cross section, showing angles and formation of cutting edges, etc. The lengths of the edges can, of course, be varied within wide limits so as to suit any required range of job sizes. The tool here described has edges 5/8th ins. long. The angles of the cutting edge may also be altered to meet any special demands.

The opposite end of rod to that carrying the handle is well rounded over and turned up in manner shown. It is desirable that the extreme tip should be nicely rounded and well polished, as this point is subjected to considerable pressures. If left blunt, or badly shaped, scarring and marking of the underside of work will result. This rounded tip, along with the two cutting edges, should then be hardened, all being well honed and polished after this operation.

The finished tool, when being used, is simply placed into the hole and the whole device turned around for a few times, until required amount of chamfering has been obtained. Removal of burrs or ragged edges of a drilled hole usually only requires

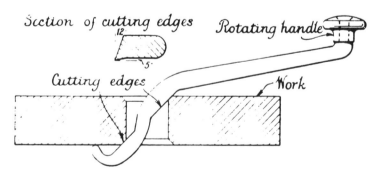

Section of cutting edges   Rotating handle

Cutting edges   Work

one or two turns of this tool. With correctly shaped and ground cutting edges, such a tool here described will speedily produce well-finished chamferings.

Holding Hacksaw Blade for Depth Slotting
(January 1924)

If a number of screw-heads or other objects require to be slotted to uniform depths, a useful idea is to prepare a blade holder after the style of that here drawn. It will use short-length blades, or broken pieces, and they can be set to project a certain distance, so the lower edges of the holder coming into contact with the screwhead determine the depth of penetration. The holder is made from flat stuff with holes at each end to pin into the usual grips of the hacksaw frame, and a turned-over flap which can be sprung in with the four screws to grip the blade firmly.

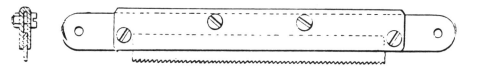

Machine Tools and Accessories

Spigot Cutter for Shouldering Rods

L.R. Turner (January 1965)

I made this tool for use in the school metalshop when we were working on a project which required quite a number of rods reduced at the ends to form a spigot or shoulder. The reduced part was to be put through a hole and riveted over.

We had two drilling machines but only one lathe. This tool speeded up the operation and left the lathe free for more important work.

Top, bottom, and back, of $\frac{1}{4}$ in. thick bright mild steel, were countersunk, riveted together and cleaned off flush. The front, also of $\frac{1}{4}$ in. b.m.s., with the $\frac{1}{4}$ in. Whitworth clamping screw, was pivoted and secured by a $\frac{1}{8}$ in. locking pin.

This construction simplifies the changing of cutters and the cleaning. The cutter is a $\frac{1}{4}$ in. square lathe bit, ground as a knife tool, with the cut adjusted by the 2 BA screw. I found the setting by trial and error. When the size was right I kept a sample spigot for future use as a setting gauge. I made bushes to take stock of $\frac{1}{4}$ in.; $\frac{5}{16}$ in. and $\frac{3}{8}$ in. dia.

The cutter is held in a machine vice on the drill table and the work in the drill chuck.

(See sketch overleaf.)

Tip from Canada

Sir, — In looking over Mr Westbury's dandy little milling machine I am reminded of the way in which I made a drilling appliance.

By casting on angle plates to the parts that could benefit from their addition — all the parts that attach to the column — the machining of the holes was easy with a boring bar between centres. (See my sketch, p. 79.)

As I have not seen this method described I thought that I might mention it at this time. It certainly saves many headaches in getting the holes bored right. Finally cut them off and use them as angle plates.

(September 1964) Fred Massey

Small Bench Grinder

F. Young (December 1935)

Most model engineers appreciate the value of a grinding head, and are only deterred from installing one on account

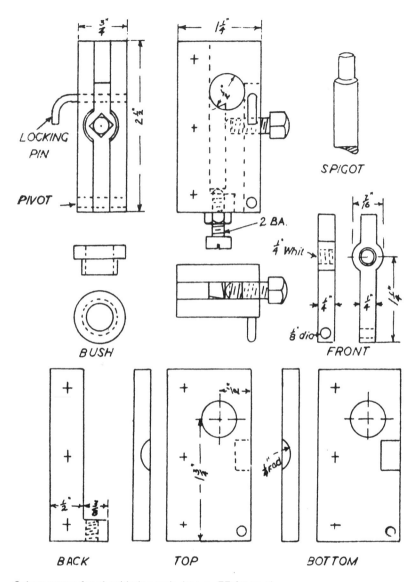

LOCKING PIN

PIVOT

SPIGOT

2 BA.

BUSH

¼" Whit

⅞" dia

FRONT

BACK

TOP

BOTTOM

Spigot cutter for shouldering rods (see p. 77 for text).

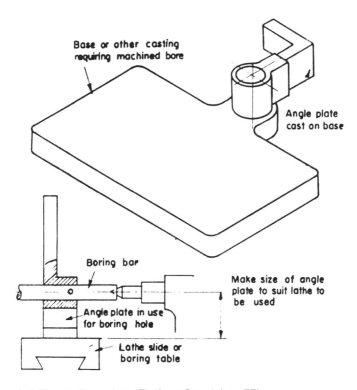

Base or other casting
requiring machined bore

Angle plate
cast on base

Boring bar

Make size of angle
plate to suit lathe to
be used

Angle plate in use
for boring hole

Lathe slide or
boring table

A drilling appliance (see 'Tip from Canada', p. 77).

of cost. To build one is not a difficult job, however, the essential point being robustness and compliance with the usual safety regulations. The drawing overleaf shows a design which the writer has just completed at a very small cost.

The main dimensions are given, and the drawing is to scale. The patterns, one for the body, one for the safety hoods, and one for the pulleys, the writer made himself. The body was cast in one piece, the caps being sawn loose when the casting came in. The cap faces were bedded down before boring, and are secured by $\frac{3}{8}$ in. B.S.F. bolts. The boring operation was the biggest in the whole

job, and involved an intricate rig-up on a small lathe, the boring tool being mounted in the headstock and the casting fed along the bed on to the tool. Special narrow type bearings carry the main shaft. The end caps were necessary, in order to locate the shaft endwise, and to keep out dust. No provision for lubrication was made, such being required in ball bearings mainly to prevent rust. Hence, the bearings were packed with good grease when assembled, and should be good for many months. Two 5 in. dia. by $\frac{3}{4}$ in. wide gritwheels were fitted, a fine one for tools and drills, and the other of a coarser nature for general rubbing

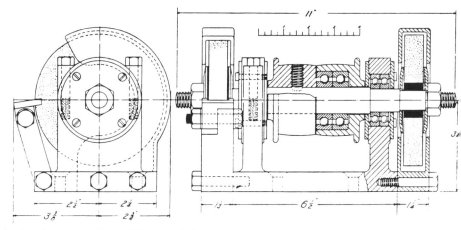

End and side elevations of bench grinder.

down jobs. A left hand thread, be it observed, is necessary at the left hand wheel, an ordinary thread sufficing at the other end.

Some soft packing medium is required between the flanges and the gritwheels, such as leather or rubber; the flanges should not bear directly upon the gritwheels on any account, and should be tight enough to hold the wheels firmly, but without cracking them. (Examine the wheels closely, and tap them to see if there are any cracks, before fitting them. Also stand clear for a few minutes when first starting up.) The wheels are usually leaded at the hole.

The tool rests were cut from steel bar stock by saw and file, and are adjustable. If more convenient, the safety hoods could also be built up from plates and riveted or welded. Extra lengths of $\frac{5}{8}$ in. B.S.F. thread are left on the main shaft in order that polishing mops may be fitted when required.

The whole machine is very compact, and can be screwed down anywhere. The writer drives his from the lathe

driving motor, and at present it is arranged to run at about 3000 r.p.m., which seems in order.

The belt striking gear, which is not shown, for throwing the belt from fast to loose pulley, was made cheaply from $\frac{1}{4}$ in. plate and angle iron.

If the drawing is studied, it will be seen that, at a pinch, the machine could be assembled with the bearing caps solid with the base, by knocking the shaft in from one end. Were he to build another, the writer would be inclined to try this method, not to gain strength particularly, but to cut out constructional work.

The machine has been in work for two months now, and has given every satisfaction.

A Tip in Grinding Copper
W.J.S. (July 1935)

Grinding copper on an emery wheel need not be such a trying job as many seem to make of it, if only the simple tip of old-time shop men is adopted. Copper, of course, is so soft that when it is ground, the emery wheel simply becomes pasted up with copper, and thus renders the cutting quality of the wheel useless. When you next have to grind a piece of copper, first cover the surface of the wheel with common lard or candle grease. The wheel should be kept covered with either of the above greases until the work is done.

Safety Washer for Grinding-wheel Spindle Nut

'Inchometer' (January 1924)

To prevent the clothing from catching in the nut of a grinding-wheel spindle, the hint depicted in the accompanying view may be followed. Instead of using a plain flat washer under the nut, have a cupped one deep enough to pass beyond the nut; the latter may be turned by a box spanner.

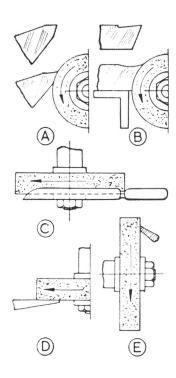

Operations in freehand grinding.

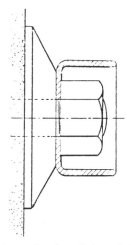

Safety washer for grinder spindle nut.

Freehand Grinding

'Geometer' (November 1955)

The advantages of a grinder over a file are that it will deal with hard materials,

scale and spots on castings and, if it is power driven, will remove material very much quicker and easier. It is, therefore, a "must" for all workshops.

In grinding data there are recommended grit sizes, bonds, and peripheral speeds for grinding wheels to be used on a wide variety of materials, but for obvious reasons it is not always possible to follow them. The amateur especially must strike a fair average.

Most general work can be done with two wheels. Reasonable sizes are between 4 in. to 6 in. dia. and $\frac{5}{8}$ in. to 1 in. width. The grit size of the roughing wheel will be between 40 and 60 and that of the finishing wheel between 80 and 100.

When speeds can be chosen, the smaller wheels should run between 4,000 and 5,000 r.p.m. and the larger between 2,500 and 3,000 r.p.m.

For general work, it is a mistake to use wheels too coarse, too fine, small or narrow. The coarse leave a rough surface; the fine overheat tools; the small run too slowly and the narrow have insufficient surface, so that parts tend to slip off the edge — with consequent damage or ground fingers!

Mounting and dressing

The wheel should be an easy sliding fit on the spindle and held between soft washers of thick paper or thin cardboard. There should be a pair of steel collars which have clearance about 1/32 in. deep on their faces, so as to grip near the outer edges. For large wheels, the rear collar may have a driving key; for small ones a frictional grip suffices. The wheel should spin truly on periphery and face.

A wheel which is eccentric, grooved, or clogged with soft metal or wood (from incorrect use) can be dressed with a hand tool consisting of a number of plain

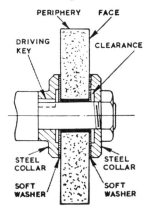

Correct mounting of the grinding wheel.

and star washers fitting loosely on a spindle; these are run in contact with the grinding wheel, as the tool is held by hand, and clean and true the periphery. In some instances, a piece of broken grinding wheel is used for minor dressing — this preferably should be of a coarse, open structure.

Maintaining truth

Efforts should be made to maintain the wheel true and clean in normal use. Corners should not be used for parts ordinarily applied to periphery or face, or they will be rounded unnecessarily and prove useless, until the wheel has been dressed, when the vital sharp-corner job turns up.

Whenever possible, the whole width of the wheel should be used, since continued application to one part produces a groove, after which the grinding of straight edges is difficult. Soft materials — wood, lead, aluminium, etc. — clog the wheel and spoil it for ordinary grinding.

Fine-edge tools should not be ground dry owing to the danger of destroying the temper and all tools should be cooled by dipping in water from time to time. Hollow grinding on the periphery of chisels A and lathe tools B is to be avoided, since the cutting edges are weakened. The face of the wheel should be used.

In sharpening instruments like knives C it is advisable to stand at the end of the spindle and make application to the periphery at the top, holding the handle firmly and drawing the blade progressively into contact.

Screwdriver blades D can be ground on the face at the front, and scissor blades E on the face at the top.

When employing tool rests, they should be adjusted close to the wheel and secured firmly, so that small or narrow parts are prevented from wedging in or being dragged through the gap.

Oiling Lathes and Machine Tools

Dear Sir, —As an old reader, I am offering the following hint and sketches in the hope that it may interest readers who possess lathes, grinders, shapers, drilling machines, etc.

There seems to me to be quite a lot of lathes and small machines about that are

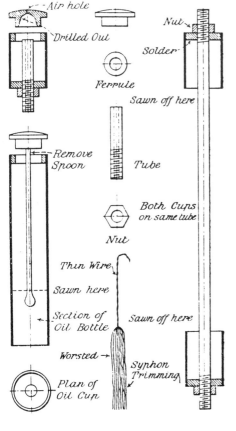

never provided with proper oiling arrangements. These kind of things seem to be regarded as "extras." Usually a hole is provided, which is either plugged up with a bit of wood, cork, or sometimes a rivet, to keep out dirt or turnings.

I wanted a pair of "syphon oil cups" for my lathe headstock bearings, and having a few old brass oil bottles by me (ex Government), I conceived the idea of utilising them for my purpose, as follows: Two of them were cut off to $1\frac{1}{8}$ ins. in length, taking the sealed ends, of course; a $\frac{1}{4}$-in. hole was drilled central through bottom and tapped. Secondly, a piece of $\frac{1}{4}$-in. diameter brass tubing was threaded both ends; a small ferrule was screwed on each end, then the parts were tinned; the tubes screwed into oil cup. Then a $\frac{1}{4}$-in. Whitworth brass nut was screwed up tight, after which the whole was sweated together over a flame.

Sufficient solder should be run into inside of cup to form bottom $\frac{1}{8}$ in. thick, to stiffen it; when cold, the tube should be sawn off level with top then drilled down to desired height.

The screwed ferrules in top of oil bottles may be taken out and sweated into top of syphon oiler. The stoppers, of course, can then be used. The latter should be drilled out as shown in sketch, and an air hole 1-16th in. or smaller should be used.

The trimmings may be made from worsted; of course, the tighter the trimming fits tube the slower it will syphon. If filled loosely it will syphon faster, of course. It is necessary to experiment a bit with the trimming in order to get it to work properly. (March 1924)   A.F. Winter

Jointing Band Saw Blades

Sir, —In the *Model Engineer* of June 23, D.C.H.G. asks about the jointing of band saw blades.

I agree that the usual method is by resistance welding but I have found that this process is inclined to make the blade very brittle at the joint. My own method for blades from $\frac{1}{8}$ in. to $\frac{1}{2}$ in. wide and used with a 10 in. band saw is to silver-solder the joints with "Easyflo," heating with an ordinary blowlamp and bevelling the ends of the blade to give as much jointing area as possible.

Heating with a blowlamp does, of course, remove the temper from the blade at the joint but I have not found that this affects the ability of the blade to cut properly or is a source of weakness.
Dar es Salaam, H.T. Lee
(September 1955)

Query—Drilling Machine Chatter

I am using a drilling machine for opening out pilot holes of $\frac{1}{8}$-in. diameter to about $\frac{3}{8}$ in., but am troubled with a chatter which is set up when the drill first starts. When once the full diameter of the drill is cutting, the action becomes smooth. Is this normal, or is there something which needs rectifying in the drilling machine, and is it likely to cause damage to the spindle assembly? The machine is one of a heavy type, with a 1-in. spindle running in 5 ball-bearings, at a speed of 340 revs. for this operation.

It is not uncommon for chatter to occur when opening out a small pilot hole. The fact is that until the drill is cutting to its full diameter, very little guidance is given to the point of the drill, and, generally speaking, the bearings of a drilling machine have not a sufficiently fine clearance to steady the drill properly.

A possible remedy would be to start the large drill on a much lower speed with heavier feed, but, unless the chatter damages the drill itself, we do not think there is any need to worry about it.

Gripping Slips for the Machine Vice

J.N. Liversage (November 1935)

Difficulty is generally experienced when holding work in the machine vice, due to the tendency to lift away from the base-plate when the jaws are tightened. The simple packing or gripping slips shown in the sketches hold work definitely down to the face of the vice with great certainty and grip, allowing heavy cuts to be taken.

The strips may be of any width or length, depending on the size of the vice. I would suggest, say, three pairs $\frac{3}{8}$ in. and $\frac{1}{2}$ in. $\times \frac{1}{8}$ in. and $\frac{3}{4}$ in. $\times \frac{3}{16}$ in. section, and of a length a little in excess of the width of jaws.

Either section shown is suitable, one being of the usual parting tool cast steel, and the other being made from parallel stock.

File off the sharp angles to about $\frac{1}{32}$ in. wide, so as not to cut into the work or the vice jaws. Case harden, if mild steel, or preferably, use cast steel, hardened and tempered.

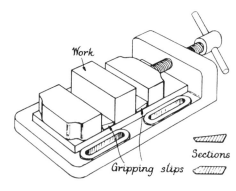

Work

Sections

Gripping slips

Simple Belt Tensioning Device
G.P. (September 1935)

The belt adjuster shown in the sketch is made from the front forks and hub of a bicycle. A piece of tube should be brazed over the spoke flanges for the belt to run on.

Provision should be made for oiling the hub. I used a piece of $\frac{3}{16}$" tube, screwed into original oil hole, and brought through one of the spoke flanges.

The gadget may be mounted in any position, and be either spring loaded, or have an adjustable arm on it.

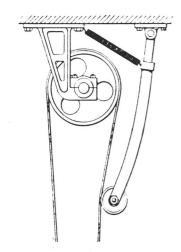

Belt Dressings
A.H.G. Vivian (September 1935)

The following recipes may prove useful to readers requiring cheap but effective belting compounds or syrups to prevent slipping. I have used them myself, and find them very satisfactory. Recipe No. 1 resembles a commercial product in character, and is used for inside dressing, to prevent slipping. When applied to the belt it acts on it in two ways; the oil softens the belt, but does not in any way injure it, as ordinary machine oils do, and in conjunction with the resin, helps noticeably in the maintenance of smooth running without slipping.

(1) 1 pint of commercial or veterinary castor oil.
$2\frac{1}{4}$ lbs. of powdered resin.

Melt together in an old jar, placed in water and brought to boiling point, taking care it does not boil over. The approximate cost for this is 2s. 0d. and the quantity is sufficient to last for months.

(2) 1 pint of old cod liver oil.
4–8 ounces of tallow.

This recipe is intended for application on the outside surface, to prevent cracking, and is intended primarily for leather belts.

Electrical

Electrical Heating Elements
R. H. Warring (February 1955)

The normal form of electrical heating element is that of a spiral of resistance wire wound on a suitable refractory former, or located within a "channel" formed in a refractory panel. The calculations involved in deciding the size and length of wire required for a given duty are quite straightforward. The best type of resistance wire for the job is 80-20 nickel-chromium alloy, as this has an exceptionally long life and can, in fact, be used up to temperatures of more than 1,000 deg. C. Nickel-iron and similar resistance wires are somewhat cheaper and can be used where element life is not so important.

Normally, working temperatures for heating elements are considered to be of the order of 500 deg. C. In practice, some parts of the element are likely to heat up more than others, particularly if shielded, and calculations based on wire temperature are usually corrected for such factors. Assuming a standard working temperature of 500 deg. F. Table I gives correction factors applicable to different types of heating elements. Thus the type of heating element mounted between mica layers, as in an electric iron, has an

equivalent working temperature of 500 × 1.5 or 750 deg. C.

Design calculations are then tackled in stages. It is convenient to design for a fixed power rating or wattage which knowing the mains voltage, enables the current carried by the element to be calculated. For example, suppose an output of 1 kilowatt (1,000 watts) is decided upon, and the mains voltage is 200. Since current = watts/volts, the current in amps is 1,000/200 = 5 amps.

Suppose, also, that we are considering the design of an element for a rod-type electric fire, where the temperature factor from Table I is 1.2. The working temperature of the element will, therefore, be 500 × 1.2 = 600 deg. C.

Resistance wires are rated according to the maximum current they will take at

Table I. Temperature factors

Type of element	Temperature factor
Fire: Rod type	1.2
Fire: Refractory base	1.0
Toaster	0.8–1.0
Kettle	1.2
Iron	1.5
Immersion heater	0.8–1.2

87

various temperatures for various diameter sizes. Such data are published by the wire manufacturers in the form of tables. Only an abridged version of such typical tables can be given here, but we have selected the range of sizes most likely to cover simple work – Table II. Using nickel-chromium resistance wire, for instance, we have to accommodate a 5-amp current flow at 600 deg. C. From the table it will be seen that 25 s.w.g. is just below this rating, whilst 24 s.w.g. rating is just above. The size required, therefore, is 24 s.w.g.

There remains only to calculate the length of this particular resistance wire to meet the original design requirements – 200 volts supply, 5 amp current consumption. Since resistance = volts/amps, total wire resistance required = 200/5 = 40 ohms.

Again reference must be made to wire tables to find the resistance of the particular size of wire chosen (24 s.w.g.) per unit length. In the case of resistance wires, resistance is usually quoted in ohms per foot, as in Table III. With some types of resistance wires, resistance is appreciably constant at different temperatures. In the case of nickel-chromium

Table II. Current rating nickel-chrome wire (current in amps)

Dia. s.w.g.	Working temperature				
	400° C.	500° C.	600° C.	700° C.	800° C.
20	7.2	8.9	11.0	13.0	15.0
21	6.3	7.6	9.0	10.0	11.0
22	5.4	6.4	7.5	8.8	9.7
23	4.4	5.3	6.2	7.2	7.9
24	3.4	4.6	5.5	6.3	6.9
25	3.3	4.1	4.8	5.6	6.1
26	3.1	3.6	4.2	4.7	5.2
27	2.6	3.3	3.8	4.4	4.6
28	2.3	2.8	3.3	3.8	4.1
30	1.9	2.3	2.6	3.0	3.3

Table III. Resistance values of nickel-chrome wire (resistance in ohms per foot)

Dia. s.w.g.	Working temperature				
	400° C.	500° C.	600° C.	700° C.	800° C.
20	0.518	0.521	0.516	0.512	0.512
21	0.655	0.659	0.653	0.648	0.648
22	0.855	0.860	0.853	0.846	0.846
23	1.17	1.17	1.16	1.15	1.15
24	1.38	1.39	1.38	1.37	1.37
25	1.68	1.69	1.67	1.66	1.66
26	2.07	2.08	2.06	2.04	2.04
27	2.49	2.49	2.47	2.46	2.46
28	3.06	3.07	3.05	3.03	3.03
30	4.36	4.37	4.35	4.31	4.31

resistance wire, this is not exactly so, and so the tables will show resistance values for different temperatures. As the temperature rises, resistance per foot tends first to increase and then decrease again. It is roughly a maximum at about 500 deg. C. Thus, taking the resistance for our calculated working temperature will produce a slightly *high* resistance value if the *actual* working temperature is somewhat higher than our original calculated value. This can be adjusted, if necessary, by making a practical test using the calculated length of resistance wire coupled up to the supply voltage and measuring the current consumption. If the actual current is lower than 5 amps, then the wire resistance is too high, and wire length can be reduced, in proportion. Normally, however, this effect can be ignored.

Thus, in our particular example, we want an element resistance of 40 ohms. The wire size is 24 s.w.g. which has a resistance of 1.38 ohms per foot at 600 deg. C. Hence the length of wire required is 40/1.38 ft. = 29 ft.

Since this is to be wound in the form of a close spiral, our final calculation is concerned with determining the physical dimensions of the spiral, i.e. diameter of the former on which the coil is to be wound, and the length of the resulting coil. One of these factors must be fixed before the other can be calculated.

Thus, if the *length* of the spiral is fixed by the physical size of the mount or firebar, etc., the internal diameter of the coil (i.e. the size of the former or mandrel on which the coil must be wound) is

$$C = \frac{d\,(3.82\,l - L)}{L}$$

where L = length of coil (inches)
d = wire dia. (inches)

C = core dia. (inches)
l = length of wire (feet)

Alternatively, if the length is not so important, but we want to fix the coil diameter as some particular size, the resulting coil length is calculated from:

$$L = \frac{3.82\,d\,l}{C + d}$$

In both cases these formulas assume that the wire is close-wound, with adjacent coils side by side. They will "spring" open slightly after winding, in practice, which effect may be allowed for, or ignored, as the case may be. This opening up of the coils does not affect the calculation, and is only mentioned as an explanation as to why the physical size of the finished "practical" coil may be larger than the calculated size.

To complete our working example with the application of the above formulas, we will suppose that the *length* of the spiral required is fixed at 12 in. Core diameter is, therefore:-

$$C = \frac{0.22\,(3.82 \times 29 - 12)}{12}$$
$$= 0.18 \text{ in.}$$

Thus, for any *larger* core diameter, there is ample wire to wind an *open* coil from the length of wire available.

If, for the second example, the core diameter was fixed as $\frac{3}{16}$ in., the length of coil would be:-

$$L = \frac{3.82 \times 0.022 \times 29}{0.1875 + 0.022}$$
$$= 11.625 \text{ in., or } 11\tfrac{5}{8} \text{ in.}$$

Query—Motor Trouble

I have a band saw which is powered by a Hoover $\frac{1}{2}$ h.p. motor controlled by an internal centrifugal switch. While using the machine recently the saw became fastened in the work and the motor stopped. Since then the motor is difficult to start – even with no load – and makes a burring noise. However, on giving a slight push with the hand, the motor quickly appears to gain full power and speed.

I took the precaution of taking the motor to a local electrician, but beyond cleaning it he does not seem to have achieved any results.

If the leads are changed over, the motor runs in the opposite direction. I have always understood that a.c. motors are not so easily reversed. (January 1957)

It would appear that the fault is in the starting windings of the motor. (This would account for the fact that when given a start it will run up to full power and run normally.) It would be fairly easy to test out the continuity of these windings to verify this matter.

With reference to the effect of changing over the leads, you will find that whether or not the leads are changed over, the motor will run in either direction according to which way it is started. It is quite impossible that the changing over of the leads can reverse the motor directly. Under normal conditions, changing the starter leads only is the method employed for reversing these motors.

Query – Running Cable to Workshop Motor

We have been recently changed over to the 230 volt 50 cycle grid system, and there is an underground cable supplying current to the garage, presumably of the same size as the enclosed sample which is used in the house. Will this be satisfactory for running a $\frac{1}{4}$ h.p. motor for driving my 3-inch lathe, and how do I make the connection from the motor to the supply in the garage? (October 1936)

The sample lead-covered twin cable sent for inspection is of 3/.029 gauge, and, according to Institution Wiring Rules, will carry up to 6.7 amperes, with a pressure drop of 1 volt for every 30 feet of lead and return – that is, 15 ft. point to point. A $\frac{1}{4}$ h.p. induction motor of reasonable efficiency will take a full load current of about 2.6 amperes on 230 volts 50 cycles, so that the cable should suffice if the distance is not too great. But it must be remembered that the starting current of single phase induction motors is very heavy, generally amounting to five or six times the full load running current at the moment of first switching on, and, therefore, the volt drop at this high current density would be fairly heavy if the cable run is considerable; and since the starting torque varies as the square of the applied voltage, the starting effort would be poor. If, on the other hand, you employ a motor of the "repulsion-induction" type, this would overcome the difficulty to a large extent, as the starting current is not nearly so heavy, and the starting torque much higher. It would have been preferable, however, if your cable size had been increased to 3./036, with a normal loading capacity of 12 amperes. All you require is a separate plug-in connection of the 3-pin type, the third pin being used for earthing the motor, and this circuit under the control of a small 15-ampere ironclad combined switch and fuse of the double pole type, the casing of which should also be earthed.

Query – Pressure-operated Switch

Can you please illustrate and describe

the principle and operation of a pressure switch as used in an air compressor plant? The particular point which I cannot understand is how the switch cuts out at a high pressure, and cuts in again at a lower pressure. (December 1954)

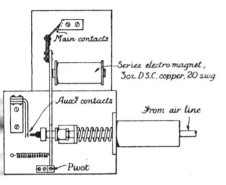

The drawing shows the arrangement of a switch of this type. The switch is operated by means of a small cylinder having a spring-loaded pressure-tight piston, or, alternatively, a diaphragm could be used.

The loading of the spring is arranged so that no movement of the piston takes place until a predetermined pressure is reached, and the end of the piston-rod is fitted with shouldered collars which pass through a slotted hole in the switch lever. At the extremity, an insulated contact-finger is fitted to the rod, so arranged that at a set pressure the rod closes the contacts of a relay switch.

Under normal circumstances, the main contacts of the motor circuit are held closed by means of an electro-magnet in series with the motor windings. The relay switch, however, short-circuits this magnet and the switch is then quickly broken.

When the pressure in the air cylinder falls by a predetermined amount, the relay contacts are first opened, but the main switch is not operated until the pressure has dropped further, when the switch lever is then pulled into contact and held by the magnet.

This particular arrangement gives positive operation and avoids chattering. It is capable of controlling a motor taking a fairly considerable amount of current.

Query — Dynamo Not Working After Repair

I recently bought a second-hand dynamo, which gave 15 volts 5 amperes. As the commutator was considerably worn, I skimmed this up true in the lathe, also fitted ball bearings in place of ring oiling plain bearings. Since these alterations, however, I can only get it to give 4 or 5 volts, and would much like to know the reason. (October 1936)

In all probability, some damage has occurred to the commutator or the windings of the armature. One of the most frequent sources of trouble after skimming up commutators is the formation of "bridges" of metal dragged across by the tool from one segment to another, setting up partial or total short-circuits in the windings. If the commutator is mica-insulated, these can generally be removed by the careful use of a fine hacksaw blade, but be careful not to get the swarf embedded in the end windings. Even with one pair of segments short-circuited like this, small generators will often fail to excite themselves. If the bridge is only a film of metal, it will often burn itself out when running, but in order to get the machine to generate any current, it will be necessary to separately excite the fields from a 12-volt battery, and run it at a fairly high speed. If any of the armature coils appear to be getting hot, stop the run at once and examine the commutator bars which are attached to the overheated coil or coils, as that will be the source of the trouble. One other suggestion may be made, and that is, if the dynamo has a brush-rocker, this may have accidentally been moved out of its correct position when refitting the bearings. Also, examine carefully the armature connections to the back of the commutator, and see that these have not been broken away or cut through in skimming up the surface. Sometimes a badly-fitted commutator is shifted out of its original position when the commutator is faced up, which either breaks away the armature connections or throws the brushes out of position to function properly.

Query — Wrong Direction

I have a small motor which runs very well, but not in the direction which I require. It works off the 240 volt mains a.c. only. The rotor is solid, and the only windings are the field windings on four poles spaced at 90 deg. to each other. I would be very grateful if you could help me in this matter. (April 1965)

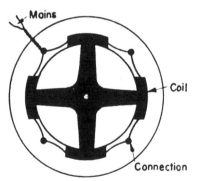

It would appear from your sketch that this is an induction motor. If it does not have separate starting windings in addition to the main coils, the field poles are probably provided with shade rings —

either solid bands or thick windings round a part of each. To reverse such a motor, field laminations must be changed around bodily. Sometimes the rotor can be reversed in its bearings, or the bearing end plates changed round, to effect the same purpose.

Induction motors which are equipped with starting windings will usually reverse if the connections of these windings are changed over in relation to the main field coils.

Query — Small Solenoids

I want to make a number of small solenoids to work off a standard bell transformer, 6 volts a.c. I understand that there is a difference between a.c. solenoids and those working off d.c.

I shall be grateful if you will tell me how to make the solenoids and what winding to use. The power required is very small, to strike a small bell once. (February 1965)

Solenoids for operation on an alternating current differ from those used for direct current working, but all that you need here is a straightforward coil and core. As the force is only to strike a bell you will use a bobbin and a sliding core, the core being controlled by a spring at one end to return it after it has acted. Make the bobbin from a short length of fibre tube, $\frac{5}{16}$ in. bore and 1 in. long inside the cheeks which are $\frac{5}{8}$ in. dia. and $\frac{1}{16}$ in. thick, and are glued on to the tube.

The core is a length of soft iron rod $\frac{1}{4}$ in. dia. and about $1\frac{1}{2}$ in. long. It should have a tapped hole at each end to take a rod to support it in the tube. The rods are accommodated in two brackets at each end of the coil; a bent up U bracket is suitable.

You have a choice of two windings. If the current is to be on for a long time, wind on 888 turns of 30 s.w.g. enamel-covered copper wire; if the period is to be short, 416 turns of 26 s.w.g. will do.

Query — Horsepower of Motor

I have an induction motor (unmarked) which runs well on 240 v. at 1450 r.p.m. There are 24 slots in the stator and the rotor size is $3\frac{1}{2}$ in. dia. $\times 2\frac{3}{4}$ in. with 29 slots.

Would you please tell me the horsepower? (August 1965)

Assuming that it is a split-phase induction motor and is self-starting, then the horsepower would be best determined by checking the current consumption.

Delco made a $\frac{1}{8}$ and $\frac{1}{4}$ h.p. motor, using the same frame which had 24 slots in the stator and was of the same physical dimensions as you have quoted. The only difference between the motors was the number of turns and wire gauge. Below is a list of typical full load currents of motors.

	200/220 volts	230/250 volts
0.125 h.p.	1.68 amps	1.55 amps
0.25 h.p.	2.4 amps	2.17 amps
0.166 h.p.	2.25 amps	2.02 amps
0.33 h.p.	2.9 amps	2.55 amps

Miscellaneous

Safety in the Workshop
F.G. Whitnall (March 1964)

It is difficult to lay down any hard and fast rules for the safety of groups engaged in a workshop. So much depends on the nature of the work, the individuals' knowledge and skill and the size of the room.

All workshops must have a cabinet containing First Aid for minor injuries. The cabinet should be clearly marked *First Aid* and displayed in a prominent position. Make sure that the door opens easily, and keep the cabinet well stocked with the essentials. They include one or two smaller bandages, several sterile dressings, a quantity of cotton wool, a few zinc oxide plasters and an antiseptic lotion or ointment. It is also useful to have a finger stool, a linen square for a sling, an eye bath, a pair of scissors and a packet of small safety-pins.

When power tools, lathes, grinding machines or spraying apparatus are used be sure to wear a pair of goggles or an adjustable eye-shield. For some of the jobs tackled in metalwork, a supply of asbestos gloves should be kept, in various sizes. As part of the normal working routine, apply a barrier cream to your hands and wrists before you begin work.

Where welding or soldering equipment is in use, or a forge is in place, be sure that the area is free of unnecessary gear or bystanders. A fire extinguisher and an asbestos fire blanket should be left conveniently near to the working space.

Heaters used for chemical preparations or fixatives are best left in a familiar place, well seen and separate from the immediate working area. They should be set up on an asbestos or some other heat-resistant base, and surrounded by a fire-proof guard.

Large quantities of inflammable liquids and chemicals and acids are safer left on the concrete floor of a store-cupboard. The containers should be clearly labelled and the use of the contents carefully regulated.

An acid bath needs to be covered immediately after use. Great care must be taken to prevent splashing and the inhalation of dangerous fumes.

Danger from falling gear, bulk timber, metal or other materials can be avoided by the provision of specially designed storage racks, bins or shelves.

Take another look at your workshop. Is it really designed and organised with safety uppermost in your mind?

95

Chemical Colouring of Metals
G. Woodin (April 1947)

The following are useful formulae for the chemical colouring of various metals, and have proved most useful in the making of model ships fittings, etc.

Imitation silvering of brass, copper, iron or steel
Place a globule of mercury, about the size of a pea, in a mortar, add two teaspoonfuls of powdered chalk and grind for half-an-hour until the chalk has acquired a grey colour. Moisten the end of a soft rag with methylated spirit, then take on it a small quantity of the powder. Rub this over clean surface of article to be silvered. In a few seconds a thin shimmery silver film will form on the surface which can be thickened by a further application of powder.

Dead black colouring of brass or copper
Immerse article in a liquid of 1 oz. of copper nitrate and 3 oz. of water. A small quantity of silver nitrate dissolved in this solution is said to improve colouring, but is not essential.

Black colouring of silver
Immerse in a solution of sodium sulphide.

Black colouring of zinc
Immerse in solution of antimony chloride.

Blue-black colouring of iron
Immerse in a solution of photographic hypo. An addition of a little lead acetate or nitrate to the solution improves the colouring.

Slightly shiny black surface for copper
Copper will acquire a slightly shiny black surface when immersed in a solution of ammonium sulphite 1 oz. and water

4 oz. When brass is immersed in this liquid it will take on a steely-grey colouring.

To tint aluminium blue
Dip metal in a hot, medium strong solution of caustic soda (sodium hydroxide) for a few seconds then rinse in warm water and dip in a hot solution of an aniline dye. The metal will then be permanently tinted.

Dulled aluminium
Dip metal in hot, medium strong solution of caustic soda.

Golden colouring of brass
Immerse in a very dilute solution of ammonium or sodium sulphide.

Red colouring of copper
Immerse as above. As strength of the solution varies so can almost any red, yellow, brown or black colour be obtained on the metal.

Tinting brass
Brass can be given tints varying from pale gold to pink and pale blue by immersing in a solution of $\frac{1}{2}$ oz. each of lead acetate and hypo to 1 pint of water.

Greying iron
Iron can be given a grey colour by boiling for half-an-hour in a weak solution of iron phosphate.

What Metal Is It?
R.H. Warring (July 1955)

In the model engineer's workshop, in particular, odd pieces of metal may well lose their identity, and selection of the required, or best, material for a particular job may become something of a problem. The familiarity which comes with long experience in the handling of metals leading to identification by appearance, or simple scratch tests, is denied to most —nor is it always conclusive enough. The alternative, chemical analysis, is a laboratory job. Somewhere between the two lie the simple, practical tests which, if not one hundred per cent. accurate, will provide quick "workshop" tests for identification suitable for most requirements.

To assist identification there are several methods of broadly classifying the various metals in common use. Some authorities advocate initial classification in weight groups—very heavy metals, heavy metals, average weight metals, and so on. This is a logical classification, as far as it goes, but in dealing with odd shapes and odd sizes—and bearing in mind the considerable errors possible in "guess-timating" densities—this is not always for the amateur. Another general classi-fication is by colour—very useful in the case of metals with a definite colour, such as brass, copper, etc., but less useful when dealing with the "white" metals unless familiar with the typical appearance of, say, silver as opposed to tin, aluminium, etc.

Although we shall make use of these two classifications to a limited extent, the best approach appears to be to con-sider two general classifications—ferrous metals and non-ferrous metals. The former should be taken to include ferro-magnetic metals (i.e. metals attracted by a permanent magnet) and so will en-compass most irons and steels, nickel and cobalt. Separation of this group by the "magnet test" is by no means infal-lible, however, as quite a number of stainless-steels, for example, are non-magnetic but are still essentially ferrous metals. In fact, if you *know* the metal is stainless-steel, a magnet will quickly show whether the stainless is of the normal chromium type (strongly magnetic) or the austenitic nickel-chrome type (non-magnetic).

A pretty reliable test for any type of stainless-steel is to place a drop of con-centrated nitric acid on the surface of the metal. If there is no chemical action, then most probably the metal is stainless-steel. Most non-ferrous metals will be attacked right away by the acid. Nickel will show a slow reaction with a pale green discoloration. Ordinary carbon-steel will show a slow reaction with a brownish black reaction. The reaction with plain carbon-steel is much quicker with dilute acid.

Another very simple test to distinguish between plain carbon-steel and stainless is to put a drop or two of strong copper sulphate solution on the surface of the metal. Metallic copper deposits readily from the solution on iron or carbon-steel whilst there is no deposit on stainless.

A fairly complete identification of the actual type of ferrous metal or alloy, or of metals or alloys likely to be confused with these materials, can be started by magnetic separation, according to whether the material is strongly magnetic, slightly magnetic or non-magnetic.

The strongly magnetic materials include carbon-steels, straight chromium stainless-steels, cast-iron, nickel and cobalt. Whether the material is a ferrous metal, nickel or cobalt can again be determined by a further magnetic test, based on the fact that ferro-magnetic materials lose their magnetism at a certain elevated temperature (known as the Curie point) and this temperature varies with different ferro-magnetic materials.

If small specimens of iron or steel, nickel and cobalt are raised to red heat, for example, none will be attracted by a magnet in this state. If the magnet is suspended close to the specimens as they are allowed to cool down, however, first the cobalt, then the iron and then the nickel will regain their magnetic properties and jump to the magnet. Differences of the order of several hundred degrees Centigrade are involved at each stage and so, using an iron nail, say, as a control, it should readily be possible to separate out the three metals concerned by such a test.

Chemical tests can also be used for separation of the ferro-magnetic materials as grouped by the initial magnet test. The surface of the specimen is cleaned and then spotted with a drop of concentrated nitric acid. No reaction is a fairly positive indication that the strongly magnetic material is straight chromium stainless-steel. Nickel, carbon-steel and cast-iron are all attacked slowly by the concentrated acid. Diluting the acid drop with an equal amount of water gives a pale greenish colour to the drop if the material is nickel, whilst a dark brown or blackish brown spot identifies carbon-steel or cast-iron.

Without care, slightly magnetic materials might be passed as non-magnetic in the initial test. For positive results the magnet should be of the modern Alnico or Alcomax type, suspended on a short length of string or thread. Bring the specimen up close to one of the pole-pieces of the magnet and watch for any movement of the magnet, indicating slight attraction.

The slightly magnetic materials most likely to be encountered are Monel and 18/8 stainless-steel. These again can be separated by spotting with concentrated nitric acid — 18/8 stainless showing no reaction, whereas a blue-green discoloration of the spot is produced with Monel. Utilisation of the Curie point effect can also be used as a second check, if required. Monel becomes non-magnetic

at a temperature somewhat less than 100 deg. C., so immersion of the specimen in boiling water and then retesting with a magnet whilst still hot will show complete loss of magnetism, if the specimen is Monel. Stainless does not lose its slight magnetism when heated to the boiling point of water.

Both Monel and 18/8 stainless, however, may also show up as definitely *non*-magnetic during the initial magnet-separation test. Other metals and alloys which come into this group include constantan, nickel-chromium, nickel-silver, nickel-copper, inconel, illium, permanickel and the nimonic alloys.

Spotting with concentrated nitric acid is again a good start to further sub-division of this group. No reaction is an indication of 18/8 stainless — or inconel or one of the nimonic alloys. Stainless can be identified from amongst these possibilities by applying a drop of cupric chloride solution in hydrochloric acid to a fresh (clean) part of the metal and leaving to react for a minute or so. Then dilute the drop with several drops of distilled water, leave for another minute and wash off. If the specimen is stainless a deposit of copper will have been formed at the base of the spot.

Where a reaction is obtained with the nitric acid spot test, then the colour of the resulting spot is an excellent criterion for further grouping. A black discoloration is an indication of Monel S. A blue-green colour indicates Monel, a copper-nickel alloy, nickel-silver alloy or constantan. In such cases the spot also appears cloudy. A clear, pale green discoloration indicates nickel or dura-nickel. A *cloudy* pale green spot indicates permanickel or Hastelloy B. A yellowish spot indicates Hastelloy A, or cadmium. A white spot is a probable indication of tin. In the case of a vigorous reaction with plenty of gassing but no marked coloration, most probably the metal is zinc.

In the case of the metal groups which produce a green or blue discoloration under the nitric acid spot, the presence of copper in the alloy can be detected with an iron nail. Clean the head of the nail and rub in the acid spot, adding a drop or two of distilled water to enlarge the spot, if necessary. If copper is a constituent element of the alloy, metallic copper will "plate" out, either on the surface of the specimen or on the head of the nail. Copper-nickel alloys and Monel are indicated by this test.

Simple chemical tests of this nature can be expanded to a degree, employing different reagents, for more positive identification of individual specimens, if required. For example, Hastelloy B and permanickel can be "separated" by spotting with hydrochloric acid and potassium ferricyanide. The resulting drop is dull green in colour with a permanickel specimen and black with Hastelloy B.

The full range of such tests is, however, far too lengthy to include in a single article. Probably the most useful form in which they can be presented is a series of charts arranged in the form of a "family tree," sub-dividing main groups by individual tests until all the possibilities named in the original group have been separated out. Charts of this kind have been prepared by the International Nickel Company of New York, and also the Mond Nickel Company in this country. Other sources have given slightly different procedures for simple identification tests but all rely, principally, on magnet tests and "spot" tests with chemical reagents.

Identification of many non-ferrous metals can be attempted direct by their colour and many also, rather more roughly, by their density. The strongly coloured metals comprise, mainly, copper and the various copper alloys — a reddish or reddish-brown colour identifying copper, a dark yellow a bronze and a light yellow a brass. The true colour, of course, can only be observed on a clean metal surface and not one discoloured or stained by oxidation or corrosion or surface dirt.

Starting with copper, the type of copper can readily be determined by "spotting" a drop of ferric chloride in acid solution on the surface (ferric chloride solution in water, plus added hydrochloric acid). A dark spot indicates that the copper is of the phosphoric or arsenical type. No reaction indicates high-purity copper (99.99 per cent.).

Brasses are best identified by dissolving a little of the metal in strong nitric acid and boiling. If a fine white precipitate appears, that indicates the presence of tin in the alloy, and so the metal is probably Naval brass or Admiralty metal. The absence of tin indicates that the metal is probably yellow brass, (copper and zinc alloy).

Bronzes can be treated in a similar manner, testing first for tin (tin bronze). If a jelly-like substance is formed instead of a precipitate, however, then most likely the metal is silicon bronze. The presence of lead can also be confirmed by filtering either of the solutions arrived at by the first test and adding strong sulphuric acid to the filtrate. A white precipitate, which may be delayed in forming, indicates the presence of lead. The absence of a precipitate in this further test indicates aluminium bronze (colour ?), red brass (colour ?) or beryllium copper.

The "white" metals can be analysed in a similar, simple manner. Probably the best method of basic separation is by density or weight, in three groups—the light metals and alloys, average density metals and heavy metals. In the first group comes aluminium and aluminium alloys and the magnesium alloys.

Separation of aluminium or an aluminium alloy from a magnesium alloy is fairly-straightforward. Clean the surface of the specimen and "spot" with a drop of weak silver nitrate solution. Leave for a minute or so and then observe what reaction, if any, has taken place. A black discoloration of the metal surfaces indicates that it is a magnesium alloy. There is no reaction on the surface of aluminium or an aluminium alloy.

Further "separation" by simple chemical tests is rather out of the question, owing to the diversity of different light alloys which may be encountered. High strength alloys can be identified by their greater hardness (e.g., resistance to scratching)—dural, for example, is appreciably stiffer and harder than pure aluminium and so an "unknown" specimen could be compared for scratch-resistance, using an iron nail, alongside known specimens of pure aluminium and dural. Alclad may be identified by its soft, easily scratched surface with a hard, scratch-resistant core.

Identification of the common medium-density metals, such as tin, zinc, nickel, etc., has already been dealt with to some extent, since these are commonly associated with, or confused with, ferrous metals. Identification of zinc should be quite easy with its ready tendency to dissolve and "gas" when spotted with nitric acid or dilute hydrochloric acid. Tin also reacts vigorously with nitric acid to give a white precipitate. The most common forms of pure tin are tinplate and tinfoil, its other widespread use being an alloying element combined with other metals.

Tinfoil and aluminium foil can be "separated" quite easily by rolling up into a small ball and heating on a charcoal block with a blowpipe. Tinfoil

Identification of copper, brass and bronze

Identify by colour	Reagent	Reaction	No reaction
Copper	Ferric chloride	Arsenical copper Phosphorus deoxidised copper	High purity copper
Brass	Nitric acid	Test for tin— Admiralty metal Test for aluminium— aluminium brass	Yellow brass
Bronze	Nitric acid	White precipitate— tin bronze Jelly formed— silicon bronze	Indefinite—(1)* Leaded bronze Aluminium bronze Beryllium copper
	(1)*Filter and add Sulphuric acid	White precipitate— Leaded bronze	Aluminium bronze (2)* Beryllium copper
		(2*)White	Aluminium bronze

melts readily and forms a metallic bead. The aluminium foil tends to oxidise and crumble into a white powder rather than melt.

Pure tin and lead are both silvery white metals, although with a colour difference. Lead is the heavier and softer and will mark paper, whereas tin will not. The lead content of a solder may be estimated, roughly, both by the stiffness of the solder and its ability to mark paper.

Silver, normally, can be identified from most other "white" metals by its colour, although it tarnishes readily when exposed to corrosive atmospheres. A possible point of confusion is that many "silvered" articles are now produced by high-vacuum deposition of aluminium, which produces a similar mirror-like appearance.

Lead, bismuth and molybdenum can readily be "separated" by spotting with acetic acid. Only lead of these three metals is attacked. Bismuth can be identified from molybdenum since it is attacked by nitric acid, whereas molybdenum is not. This is standard procedure for the identification of these three heavy "white" metals, when the specimen is known to consist of one of them.

Identification of the rarer heavy metals, such as used for decorative or protective plating, etc., is rather more complicated. With the exception of gold, all the metals likely to be encountered are "white." Gold can be identified by colour, with a further check, if necessary, that it does not give any reaction when spotted with any concentrated acid. It is, of course, dissolved by boiling aqua regia.

Boiling a small amount of the specimen in aqua regia is also the standard test procedure for "separating" the heavy white metals. Palladium and osmium are attacked rapidly. If identified by this means, the surface of the specimen can then be spotted with concentrated nitric acid and dimethylglyoxime — palladium giving a yellow precipitate and osmium none.

Tungsten and platinum are attacked slowly by boiling aqua regia. A further spot test separates the two — warm nitric acid and hydrofluoric acid producing a brown colour with tungsten but none with platinum.

Iridium, rhodium, ruthenium and tantalum are not appreciably attacked by boiling aqua regia. Tantalum, however, is attacked by hydrofluoric acid, whereas

Identification of the rarer metals

Test	Reaction	No reaction
Boil in aqua regia	Slow attack — platinum or tungsten (1) Rapid attack — osmium or palladium (2)	Tantalum, rhodium, (3) iridium
(1) Soak in HNO_3 and HFl	Brown colour — tungsten	Platinum
(2) Soak in HNO_3 add dimethyl-glyoxime	Yellow precipitate — palladium	Osmium
(3) Spot with HFl	Attacked — tantalum	Rhodium, iridium (4)
(4) Add boiling H_2SO_4	Attacked — rhodium	Iridium

the other metals in this group are not. Similarly rhodium is attacked by boiling sulphuric acid, whilst iridium and ruthenium are not. Further separation of the latter is not possible by simple tests, unless a sufficient quantity is available for a reasonably accurate determination of the density of the specimen. Iridium is roughly twice the density of ruthenium.

Making Oilcans
B. Kitchen (August 1970)

The following method of making oil cans from the polythene flasks sold with after shave lotion and other toilet preparations may be of interest.

A brass plug is turned a tight push fit in the neck of the bottle or flask and the outer portion turned to the shape of the spout or nozzle required. If the end of the nozzle is threaded 4 BA and a cap turned to fit, from a stub of brass rod, the bottle will be leakproof.

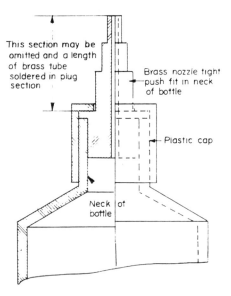

This section may be omitted and a length of brass tube soldered in plug section

Brass nozzle tight push fit in neck of bottle

Plastic cap

Neck of bottle

The original plastic cap is bored out to clear the brass nozzle as shown in the drawing. If desired a brass tube may be soldered into the brass plug, so doing away with having to turn the nozzle, and this tube may be any length required.

Warning: when using go easy on the pressure as a good squeeze can send a jet of thin oil shooting across the workshop.

Make Your Own Modelling Clay
C.H. Hancock (May 1965)

I would like to contribute a little information to S.W.C. of Somerset who inquired about plasticisers for clay.

Formula I:
    100 mesh Florida Kaolin . . 67 parts
    finely ground sulphur . . . . 33 parts
Formula II:
    Clay . . . . 55 parts
    Sulphur . . . . 25 parts
    Lithopone . . . . 20 parts
To either of the above formulae add:
1. No. 2 Petroleum
2. No. 3 Cup Grease . 50 per cent
    National Refing T & R Grease . .
    . . . . 50 per cent
3. Palm oil . . . . 80 per cent
    Japan wax . . . . 20 per cent
4. Lanolin . . . . 60 per cent
    Glycerine . . . . 40 per cent
5. Lanolin . . . . 60 per cent
    Palm oil . . . . 20 per cent
    Glycerine . . . . 20 per cent
6. Palm oil . . . . 80 per cent
    Lanolin . . . . 20 per cent

Add enough of one of the above vehicles to the clay to obtain the desired plastic quality. This will prove to be about one part vehicle to three parts of dry mixture.

Earth colours may be used for colouring. Eye strain is lessened with a grey-green colour. Chromium oxide, burnt sienna, chrome yellow and many others may be used for pigmentation. Take care to avoid poisonous pigments, (which are quite often the yellow ones like lead chromate, zinc chromate and lead ammoniate).

The actual plasticine is made in Italy and is a mixture of tallow, powdered sulphur and native Italian earth with the addition of earth colours to produce the characteristic grey-green colour. Sometimes oleic acid is added to this mixture.

S.W.C. might like to experiment with his own mixtures of non-hardening clay. In this case, it is done by using;

1. Clay—finely ground or air floated.
2. Inert filler—sulphur.
3. Vehicle—various plasticisers.
4. Pigment—earth colours.

White English china clay should be a good start. The Italian plasticine (plastilina) is furnished in three grades: *coarse*, *medium* and *fine*. The coarse is used for heroic size modelling and the fine for small work.

Aside from getting the right plastic "feel" to the mixture it is a vexing problem to get the proper mixture of plasticisers which will not become a sticky mess in hot weather and comparatively unyielding in cold weather.

In addition to the above, it might be noted that there is a modelling clay on the American market which hardens a few hours after opening the container and which may be further hardened by placing in the kitchen oven for a short while. During modelling it can be made more plastic by adding a small amount of water. I would suppose that this material is a mixture of clays with perhaps some iron oxide powder plus a water soluble plastic vehicle. Perhaps polyvinyl alcohol may be a basis for this vehicle.

Query—Sand for Moulding

I have just made a small furnace capable of melting iron, but I should be glad of some advice regarding the sand used for making moulds.

(1) What is the composition of this sand?

(2) What are cores made of?

(3) Could the same sand be used for moulds for brass casting?

(4) Is it possible to use plaster of paris instead of sand for moulds?

(1) The basis of moulding sands is usually what is known as "green" sand, but any clean fine-grade sand can be used, provided that it is free of chemical impurities, such as salt, which is usually found in sand obtained at the seaside. Specially selected and prepared sand is obtainable from dealers in foundry supplies.

Various substances are often added to sand to make it more suitable for moulding, including brick dust, dry clay powder, etc. The sand must be just sufficiently damp to cohere firmly, but excess moisture must be avoided.

(2) Cores are made from the same sand, in some cases with additions of oil or gum to make it more adhesive.

(3) The same sand can be used for brass moulding.

(4) Plaster of paris is not suitable for ordinary moulds, owing to difficulty of providing sufficient air venting to release the gases in the molten metal, but plaster moulds are used under certain circumstances, for casting by the method known as the "Lost Wax Process."

Hand Cream

Sir,—A correspondent asked recently for some method of getting and keeping his hands clean. I enclose a recipe which I use myself in the workshop.

The ingredients are: $\frac{1}{2}$ lb. granulated gum arabic, dissolved in $\frac{1}{2}$ gal. hot water; $2\frac{1}{2}$ lb. soap chips dissolved in $\frac{3}{4}$ gal. hot water; 1/3 lb. Lanolin; 1 tablespoonful glycerine and 1 tablespoonful boric acid.

Mix the solution of gum arabic and soap chips and work the Lanolin into the slowly cooling mixture. Stir in the glycerine and boric acid and pour into glass jars.

A heaped teaspoonful of the cream worked into the hands and wrists when they are clean will protect them from grime and dirt. The Lanolin fills the pores and the gum arabic seals them. Boric is one of the best antiseptics and will prevent cuts and scratches from becoming infected. After work the accumulated dirt can be worked loose with the fingers using a few drops of water. Then rinse and wash the hands. The ingredients of this formula can be compounded in any kitchen.

(December 1955)   J.A. Watson

P.T.F.E.

Sir,—With reference to the warning of the risk to health when machining P.T.F.E. contained in Mr A. Ward's letter (M.E. February 7), may I quote from I.C.I.'s publication ''Medical Aspects of Polytetrafluoroethylene''?

'' 'Fluon' (polytetrafluoroethylene) is an inert, non-toxic thermoplastic polymer— it has a working temperature range of + 250 deg. C (+ 482 deg. F) down to at least liquid nitrogen temperature—it is being used in this and other countries for surgical uses. The polymer produces no skin irritation or sensitisation and no reaction when implanted in living tissues. It is harmless when ingested daily by experimental animals over a period of months.

''When heated to temperatures above 250 deg. C (482 deg. F) it begins very slowly to decompose—above a temperature of 400 deg. C (752 deg. F) the amount of decomposition products increases more rapidly but, until the temperature reaches 450—500 deg. C (842— 932 deg. F) is still insufficient to make possible accurate identification of all the substances so formed.

''People inhaling the fumes develop a characteristic syndrome with influenza-like features. The signs and symptoms follow a latent interval of a few hours, are always evanescent in character and invariably subside within 24—28 hours with no after effects.

''Workmen can be affected, however, by smoking tobacco contaminated by the powder—a few particles of the powder on the end of a lighted cigarette may be sufficient to produce the illness. High speed machining of the polymer is an unlikely way of producing the fumes since it is improbable that sufficient polymer is subjected to a high enough temperature to produce enough localised fumes for this purpose. Most of the cases previously thought to be due to machining were almost certainly caused by smoking at work or by contaminating hands or clothing with powder subsequently transferred to the tobacco.

''The National Advisory Council for Aeronautics in the U.S.A. issued a memorandum on the safety regulations for machining 'Fluon' P.T.F.E. and this document mentioned the death of a machinist who had smoked a cigarette contaminated by the polymer. Detailed and intensive investigation—has shown that the assertion was completely without foundation—in this country the Minister of Labour stated in the House of Commons that H.M. Government had no knowledge of such an incident.

"The plastic has been used for surgical appliances with encouraging results. It has been subjected to a more thorough investigation than many comparable materials and the facts suggest that its hazards have been misinterpreted and exaggerated."

I hope this information will be of use to readers, and allay any unnecessary fears. In conclusion I would like to state that I have no connection whatever with I.C.I. or any other plastics manufacturer, but I have been a reader of M.E. since 1929, and in common with many other readers miss the "Column of Live Steam." Best wishes to those who are carrying on with the good work.
(June 1969)   P.A. Wood

Metric System

Sir,—Your correspondents of the past few months have expressed a number of interesting opinions on the advantages and disadvantages of "going metric." Most of these writers have presented what I would consider confused statements of the facts and the time would now appear ripe for clarification.

Two issues are involved: firstly the use of decimal notation instead of fractional, and secondly, the use of the metric units system (SI preferably) instead of the British system. Dealing with the notation question first, current practice in British countries is to use both fractions and decimals as convenient. Calculations are most often done using decimals whereas dimensions and ratios are generally expressed as fractions depending on the order of accuracy required. The metric system per se does not prohibit the use of fractions, although most metric dimensions are commonly expressed in decimals.

As to units, I have used the words British and metric rather than FPS and MKS advisedly, as the present British engineering system is not the FPS system. In fact it is a system of units developed for convenience of users and is based on the slug as a unit of mass, the pound weight as a unit of force, the foot, and the second. All the preferred units refer to these basic quantities only, the non-preferred units, rod, pole, perch, etc., are rapidly being dropped, with the exception of certain persistent units such as gallons, h.p. and inches. Again, the metric system in use is not the MKS system, far from it, but if the SI system is introduced there will exist a fair approximation to a pure MKS system. The deviations will consist in the use of terms such as Newtons to refer to metre kilograms sec^{-2}, litres instead of cubic metres, etc. The electrical units in use are common to both systems.

Thus two basic differences are apparent between the opposing systems, firstly the size of the units, and secondly, the conversion factors between the preferred unit and its derived submultiple. These factors are easily remembered powers of ten for the SI system and equally easily remembered constants for the British system. If preferred units are used these factors are few. A further difference exists in the method of introduction of the gravitational acceleration "G."

The desirability of using each system should now be considered: Dimensional units and notation are used in four main areas viz.: general conversation, commerce, pure science and engineering. In general conversation there is little place for decimal notation and fractions will be retained at least to express ratios or awkward quantities. In commerce too, fractions will probably be retained as the natural method of expressing awkward ratios. Decimal notation would no doubt aid computation. In pure science there appears virtually no case for the retention of fractions other than as constants in simple formulae.

Three factors affect the notation used in engineering. Because engineering is the interface between pure science and, shall I say, the layman, it must use notation common to both sides in order to communicate effectively. Because it is concerned more than most with ratios, e.g., in scaling, it must retain fractions for convenience. Because the decimal notation is acknowledged to be an aid to computation it also must be employed. Thus fractions and decimals must be retained together as acceptable notation.

The problem of the physical dimensions of objects, as for example shown on drawings, is a little more complicated. This is the province almost solely of the engineering and allied professions and for that reason only, based on the argument above, fractions and decimals could be retained. The matter is somewhat deeper however. It hinges in fact, on the method by which measurements are made, their inherent accuracy and the system of units employed. Measurements in the order of a foot are generally made using a foot scale subdivided into inches and fractions of an inch down to 1/32. There are two reasons for this. Firstly decimal notation would require, for accuracy, graduations below 1/10 inch, i.e., to 1/100 of an inch, which is a little too small for easy reading. Secondly, the required order of accuracy in parts of this size is about ± 1/64. Thus fractional inch notation satisfies two requirements; decimal inch would not. Note that millimetre notation also satisfies these requirements.

In items smaller than a foot, say from six inches downwards, the required order of accuracy increases and decimal notation becomes the more practicable. Our instruments are then appropriately graduated. A strong case exists for the use of drawing notation relevant to the instruments to be used and therefore for the retention of both fractions and decimals, if feet and inches are retained.

Consider now the desirability of using either of the systems of units. I have said that the differences consist basically in the size of the few units involved and in the few conversion factors for submultiples. This statement applies to the British engineering system and not to that employed by laymen, commerce or physicists. These groups, who are not so concerned with the problem, have not felt it necessary to rationalise the FPS system as have engineers. Physicists in fact employ the MKS system almost solely. If one can mentally adapt to the change in the size of the units, and this is not difficult, the only remaining difference is that of conversion factors. (Admittedly the metric system is based on units which have a highly impracticable origin whereas the British units have been developed to describe the sizes of common items.) These conversion factors apply, in the engineering system, only to the conversion from preferred to non preferred units, e.g., from ft lb sec −l to h.p., cu. ft. to gallons, feet to inches, and whilst they represent a more difficult calculation than division by a multiple of ten they are less easily lost during computation. Or perhaps are more easily found again.

Summarising then, fraction and decimal notation must be retained in engineering and the choice of a system of units appears to depend on the dubious convenience of conversion, providing preferred units are used. The immense cost of a complete change to SI units cannot surely be justified by such an apparently small advantage, and the effort would be perhaps better spent converting commerce to a rational British system. Physicists and the like, after all, do not have much capital tied up with the system of units.

To lend weight to my argument I should perhaps say that I am a graduate aeronautical engineer employed by the Royal Australian Air Force. As such I am required to operate a French aeroplane using French, British, American, Canadian, Swiss, German and Australian drawings, tools and test equipment.

I have found that the French metric system is quite unmanageable but that the preferred units in the British and SI systems may be used simultaneously without fear. The multiplicity of preferred units in the SI system is generally ignored and the required basic unit which most conveniently describes the quantity under discussions is chosen from the appropriate system.

Finally, whilst I agree in detail, if not in principle, with Mr J. G. Steel (Postbag Sept. 19th), particularly in reference to the theoretical content and basis of articles in M.E., I strongly contest his assertion that use of the British system leads to confusion in the basic principles of engineering.

Australia   A.J. Emmerson
(January 1969)

A Simple Forge
Simpson Grant (December 1935)

A cheap and handy forge which I have just constructed is shown in the illustration. It consists of an old piece of sheet-iron beaten into a pan about 7" deep. Four angle iron legs are bolted to this to bring it to a working level, and through a hole in the pan bottom is

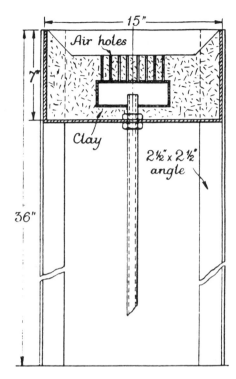

brought the air pipe, which is secured by two nuts. Pressed over the pipe end, is a circular toffee tin, in the top of which is a number of holes.

Around everything is packed fireclay; when putting the clay in, nails or wires should be run from the can holes and out of the clay, so as to leave holes in the clay also. The holes in the writer's forge are $\frac{3}{16}$", and the air pipe is connected to an old pair of bellows, which is secured to the floor and worked by the foot. The fireclay can be dished in the middle as shown.

A Simple Furnace
Neville Deane (April 1927)

The need is sometimes felt for a simple

107

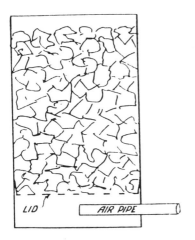

LID | AIR PIPE

solid-fuel furnace which will attain a high temperature. The furnace as described will easily reach 1,100 degrees Centigrade, *i.e.*, above the melting point of copper, and could be used for hardening small high-speed steel tools, etc.

The essential requirements are a tin—such as a cocoa tin—and a pair of bellows, foot for preference.

Take the tin lid and slit the edges with a pair of shears till the lid can be forced down into the body of the tin. Then punch plenty of holes in the lid, which will then be ready to act as the firebars. Then take the tin itself and punch a hole in the side, at the base, to take a piece of iron tube to connect to the bellows, or perhaps the nozzle of the bellows could be inserted direct. Force the lid down into the tin till it is just over the tube, as in sketch, and the furnace is complete.

To light up, use a piece of oily rag, small piece of wood, whichever comes handiest, light up and add charcoal pieces, or small coke. Charcoal is the best, but is more expensive, and has an annoying habit of crackling and flying up into one's face, especially at particularly interesting

moments. When the charcoal or coke shows signs of catching, use the bellows gently when a high temperature will soon be reached.

Two points to watch are, to use the right size of fuel—not too large or too small—and not to blow so hard as to blow the fuel out of the tin. The writer has melted copper in a furnace made as described within 15 minutes of starting up.

Casting Aluminium Alloys
A.J.T. Eyles (August 1935)

For the production of good castings in aluminium alloys, the pouring temperature is an important factor. High temperature pouring usually gives a porous casting with a dull finish. The temperature should never be allowed to rise very much above the melting point of the alloy, and the dross or slag should be thoroughly skimmed off the surface of the molten alloy. When this has been methodically done, the molten alloy should be vigorously stirred and quickly poured in a steady stream.

Although plumbago crucibles are generally regarded as the most suitable for melting aluminium alloys, they are somewhat expensive to use for making small sand castings in aluminium. Experience shows that if iron pots are kept well coated with a thin clay wash or graphite mixture (one part by volume of graphite in two parts of water), they are perfectly satisfactory for the purpose. Also, if the stirring rod is similarly treated with clay wash or the graphite mixture, there is very little danger of any material amount of iron being dissolved.

Moulds for aluminium alloys are best made from green sand, lightly rammed and dusted over with french chalk or plumbago. For the cores, either fine green sand or sawdust may be used.

Resin is frequently used as a binding agent which allows the cores to soften and crush as the alloy cools. Ordinary core gum also gives satisfactory results as a bond. Hard cores often produce cracked castings, as they do not contract to the same extent as the casting. Owing to aluminium alloys being comparatively light, many moulds are cast without being weighted down or clamped. In such cases the weight of the top box may be sufficient to resist the pressure tending to separate the box parts, but it is advisable to err on the side of safety, and, excepting on small castings, some provision should be made against a lift and the subsequent run out, because it is not only head pressure that is to be resisted, but also momentum, and the extent of the pressure thus exerted is not easily ascertained. As already indicated, the physical properties and structures of an aluminium alloy casting are influenced to an almost unbelievable extent by the melting and pouring temperatures. To get the best results, the molten alloy should be poured at as low a temperature as will ensure the mould being completely filled. The casting temperature must necessarily vary somewhat according to the thickness of the metal in the castings being made; thus a temperature that would give good results for very thin sectional model work would be too high for castings that are bulky, because the fluidity of the metal would be preserved longer, and gases are more likely to be absorbed. The surface of castings that are made when the temperature of the metal is too high is invariably discoloured, and this discoloration is also noticeable near the runners on castings that are thin.

A pyrometer is an advantage in determining the temperature, and is much better than depending upon the sight or colour of the metal. In most aluminium foundries aluminium alloys are melted under pyrometric control, and the temperature checked by immersion pyrometers. Should the molten metal become over heated in spite of frequent use of the pyrometer, the harmful effects of overheating may be minimised by the exercise of care in cooling the metal down. The molten metal should never be violently disturbed while in this state. The metal to be added should not be thrown into the molten alloy, but put in gently and quietly stirred in the centre of it, care being taken not to touch the sides of the pot, as this is apt to injure the protective coating and expose the vessel to the intensified action of the aluminium at this high temperature, introducing hard spots in the casting. Properly melted aluminium runs up sharply into moulds, but, badly melted, the metal runs faint in edges and corners, and so causes trouble. Complicated aluminium alloy castings necessitate the provision of chills, whenever there are large bosses or other masses of metal in conjunction with thinner sections. Since aluminium is only one-third the weight of brass, the runners and risers should be three times as high, but as this is impracticable, it is advisable to provide a thick cope whenever economically possible. The practice of pouring from a height with the view point of securing artificial pressure is very detrimental with aluminum, as it tends to cause porosity, blow-holes and excessive dross. It is always safer to fix a minimum pouring height by mechanical means, or arrange the moulds on girders at a natural height for pouring. By paying attention to melting practice, and due regard to the importance of casting temperature, together with good moulding practice, castings free from blow-holes, porosity, etc., are readily obtained.

Melting Aluminium

Sir, —G. M. Del in the Orange Free State has been troubled by blow-holes in aluminium castings. His troubles indicate that the aluminium is being poured too hot, and that his moulding sand may be a little too damp, causing steam to make blow-holes.

Before pouring the aluminium allow it to set in the crucible until it has cooled down, to show a dull cherry red, in poor light, on the outside of the crucible, for fairly light castings, and to a dull cherry to black for castings of one half-inch or more in thickness. This cooling will also help to reduce shrinkage.

I use either a cast iron melting pot or a steel pot made from a short length of 4 in. pipe with a bottom welded in. Both are all right for aluminium.

A little clean sand or finely broken glass sprinkled over the molten aluminium while it is cooling helps to eliminate the gases.

The metal should be skimmed before it is poured.

I would recommend the use of Foseco degassing tablets. They give a finer grain structure and greater strength to the castings, beside removing most of the porosity.

Alberta   D.A. Lefever
(January 1965)

[*Here a reader not far east of the Rocky Mountains helps another reader in Africa. Internationalism is much discussed today: in these pages it is quietly and naturally practised.* —Editor.]

Measurement of High Temperatures

A.H. Stuart, Ph.D., B.Sc. (March 1927)

A reader of *The Model Engineer* has written to the Editor asking if particulars can be given of an easily made pyrometer. This is not a question which is readily answered, for it depends mainly upon the precise meaning of the terms "easily made," and also to a large extent upon the range and degree of accuracy expected of the instrument. The most satisfactory procedure appears to be to provide a brief description of the methods commonly employed for recording high temperatures and leave it to those most interested to decide whether a pyrometer constitutes "practical politics."

It may be interesting in the first place to set out the various types of temperature measuring instruments with the limits of temperature over which their range usually extends in practice. The centigrade scale will be used throughout. If anyone prefers the Fahrenheit scale, the numbers may, of course, be readily transformed by dividing by 5, multiplying by 9, and adding 32.

Method	Range in degrees C.
Expansion Thermometers—	
Mercury in glass	− 39 to 500
Mercury in silica	− 39 to 600
Gas thermometers	up to 1,200
Electric Pryometers—	
Platinum resistance	− 100 to 1,100
Thermocouples (platinum alloys)	300 to 1,400
Thermocouples (base metals)	− 100 to 1,100
Total Radiation Pyrometers	500 to 1,400
Optical Pyrometers	600 to 3,500

To obtain a correct idea of the significance of the above table, the following records of temperatures may be useful:-

	Degrees C.
Water boils	100
Tin melts	232
Lead melts	327
Mercury boils	357
Zinc melts	419
Aluminium melts	657
Zinc boils	918
Silver melts	961
Gold melts	1,062
Copper melts	1,083
Cast iron melts	About 1,100
Pure iron melts	1,500
Fire brick softens	1,400 to 1,800
Silica softens	1,500
Platinum melts	1,750
Iron boils	2,450
Tungsten melts	3,000

Temperature of sources of heat:-

	Degrees C.
Bunsen burner flame	about 1,200
Petroleum blowpipe flame	" 1,500
Oxy-hydrogen blowpipe flame	" 2,000
Oxy-acetylene blowpipe flame	" 2,400
Electric arc	" 3,500

Table for judging temperatures by appearance:-

	Degrees C.
Very dull red	About 500
Dull red	" 700
Cherry red	" 900
Orange	" 1,100
White	" 1,300
Dazzling white	1,500 or above

Low-temperature Solders

Dear Sir, — With further reference to the recent query on this subject by "P.L." (Wakefield), I list below a range of low-melting point solders that may be of use to him.

Woods: Lead 25 per cent., tin 12.5 per cent., bismuth 50 per cent., cadmium 12.5 per cent. Melting point, 140 deg. F.

Lipowdry: Lead 29.9 per cent., tin 12.7 per cent., bismuth 50 per cent., cadmium, 10.4 per cent. Melting point, 150 deg. F.

Expanding: Lead 66.7 per cent., bismuth 8.3 per cent., cadmium 25 per cent. Melting point, 150 deg. F.

D'Arcot's: Lead 25 per cent., tin 25 per cent., bismuth 50 per cent. Melting point, 200 deg. F.

Rose's: Lead 28.1 per cent., tin 21.9 per cent., bismuth 50 per cent. Melting point, 203 deg. F.

Cast's: Lead 31.25 per cent., tin 18.75 per cent., bismuth 50 per cent. Melting point, 218 deg. F.

Sir Newton's: Lead 30.0 per cent., tin 20.0 per cent., bismuth 50 per cent. Melting point 212 deg. F.

In melting, the tin should always be melted first as being the higher temperature of the range.

J.W. Cooper

Query — Glass Grinding

Can you inform me how to polish the cut edges of glass, and is this within the scope of the amateur workshop? I have made a clock face of glass and wish to polish the edges, but the methods I have tried so far only seem to make things worse.

It is certainly possible to carry out this work within the scope of the amateur workshop, but the process is a very slow one.

Unless optical methods of grinding the glass are available, the rough surface left by cutting must first be ground smooth using a fairly sharp abrasive, such as carborundum, which may be used on a lap or buffing wheel, and this is then followed up by successive stages of finer abrasives, such as flour emery, crocus and tripoli, until a sufficiently smooth and highly polished surface is obtained. The final polishing may need to be carried out with rouge, if a very high polish is necessary.

Nameplates

Sir,—Making a model traction engine, I needed some nameplates and finally obtained excellent results using Printed Circuit Board and Letraset, Blick and Brady adhesive transfer letters. The method used was as follows:

1. Gently clean the copper surface with fine steel wool.
2. Apply the required lettering using the correct size and type and rub well on.
3. Apply strip round edges and circles in the corners. If these are not available this can be done with nail polish or paint.
4. Immerse in a small dish containing slightly warmed strong solution of Ferric Chloride (obtainable at any chemist).

In about 20 minutes the nameplate may be removed when the copper should be dissolved away leaving the lettering, etc., intact. Rinse in water, rub off the adhesive lettering giving a paxolin plate with lettering and border in copper. The background may be painted and the plate attached to the model using small screws or epoxy.
(June 1969)   B.G. Slater

Query—Marking Steel Tools

Q.—I have a number of rather good quality tools which I wish to mark my name on for identification purposes. These are all hardened tools, upon which letter punches have no effect. I would be much obliged if you would suggest some means of doing this.

A.—The simplest and most effective method of marking hardened steel is by means of etching. The surface is, first of all, given a resistant coating, which may consist of a film of beeswax, applied by warming the steel and rubbing it on; alternatively, a coating of Brunswick black or any kind of acid-resisting enamel or varnish, may be used. The lettering is incised through the "resist" by means of a sharp scriber or stylus, and etching fluid applied over the area required, by means of a glass rod, or a splint of wood. For the etching fluid, a strong solution of sulphate of copper in water may be employed; this does not bite deeply, but gives a clearly visible impression by the slight deposition of copper on the steel. Its action is improved by the addition of a little common salt. For a deeper impression, either hydrochloric or nitric acid may be employed, a mixture of the two being still more powerful, but extreme care is called for in mixing such violent reagents, and only the very small amount required for immediate use should be mixed at one time.
(1936)

Extracting a Tight Pinion
H. Bland (October 1936)

Small gears, pinions, or spur gears fixed on one shaft with a key often are very difficult to remove, especially if they have been fitted a great length of time.

I have found this device most useful, and motor car owners would find it far cheaper than the special apparatus obtainable for doing this work.

For making this pinion remover, take a flat bar of steel or iron, heat and bend to the shape illustrated, its base should be slotted and tapered to allow it to be easily inserted between the pinion and

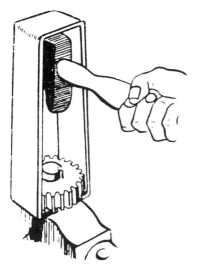

the vice where the work is held securely (see illustration).

One heavy hammer used on the inside of the upper cross piece, as indicated on the sketch, will quickly release the pinion.

Query—Etching Brass

Q.—What is the best method of obtaining a frosted or roughened effect on the centre portion of a brass clock dial?

A.—*This can be etched by means of acid and any parts required to be left bright should be painted with a resistant varnish or wax to prevent contact with the acid. Nitric acid diluted to about half strength will work fairly well on brass but for more rapid action hydrofluoric acid is generally recommended. The latter, however, is more difficult to handle, as it cannot be kept in glass bottle but only in rubber or plastic containers. The acid should be thoroughly washed off in water after the etching is completed.* (1955)

A Simple Method of Making Clock Hands
L.G.S. (July 1935)

A minute hand to match the hour hand of a grandfather clock was made from a length of 16 gauge tinned copper wire. It will be seen from the sketch that the hand is in seven pieces, six of which are wire bent to shape, and the boss is made from 16 gauge sheet brass. After neatly soldering together, the wire is flattened by light blows with a large faced hammer. If the hand is now painted black, it will be hard to distinguish it from one cut from sheet.

Making and Using Case-Hardening Compound
V.W.D.B. (September 1935)

Many workers like to make everything they use for themselves, and for these, the following recipe may be interesting. It has been well tested, as during the war case-hardening compounds were difficult to obtain, and after numerous experiments, the compound given below was found to give the best results. All carbonising compounds consist of charcoal as a base, and the best charcoal is that obtained from nuts, cherry or plum stones, coconut shells, or anything of that sort, as these make a very hard base which does not contract during the carbonising process. As most "M.E." readers will remember, plum and apple jam was one of the luxuries on which the "Tommies" were fed, and from one of the jam factories, plentiful supplies of the stones were available.

To make the charcoal on a small scale,

fill up cocoa tins with the raw stones, wire the lid down, make a small hole to allow the gas to escape. Place on a fire to gradually warm up, and finally heat to a bright red heat, till no trace of gas escapes from the vent hole.

When cold, crush, so that it will pass through a sieve with about 6 wires to the inch, making as little dust as possible. Next take 4 oz. of soda (commercially pure anhydrous carbonate of soda) and 2 oz. of barium carbonate, add $\frac{1}{2}$ pint of water, and thoroughly stir the charcoal into this mixture. Finally spread on trays, and place over the fire to thoroughly dry.

Cocoa or similar cans make quite good carbonising boxes, but can only be used once.

In packing the boxes, place about one inch of the compound at the bottom of the box, and fill up with alternate layers of the objects to be carbonised and more compound, taking care that there is an inch or more of the compound between the various items and the walls of the box. Pack as tightly as possible, and lute the lids down with "Purimachos" or some similar clay compound. The lids should be wired down. Place in the kitchen fire, and after the boxes have become thoroughly red hot, maintain that heat for six to twelve hours, according to the depth to which it is required to harden the surface.

If the strength of the core is unimportant, the objects can be immediately plunged into cold water. If, however, a thoroughly tough core is required, it is advisable to allow the objects to cool off in the carbonising box, and then to reheat to 1,650° Fahr. (cherry red heat) and quench in water. Again reheat to 1,450° (verging on cherry red), and quench in tallow or oil.

On no account should the heat during carbonising exceed 1,800°, which is a bright cherry red verging on yellow heat.

When only a slight depth of case hardening is required, what is known as the "open hearth process" can be employed.

There are two objections to this process, the first being that the core of the article is not toughened as in the former process, and the second is that a slight scale is formed during the process.

The compound required for this process is of the following composition: 1 lb. charcoal dust, 4 oz. soda ash (anhydrous carbonate of soda), 4 oz. borium carbonate, 4 oz. ferrocyanide of potassium (yellow cyanide of potassium). These should be well pounded together and ladled on to the previously heated (to a bright cherry red) article, which is then allowed to cool to a dull red heat.

This process is repeated three or four times, when it will be found that the carbonisation has penetrated to a depth of about 1/64 in.

This process serves well for drilling jig bushes and the like, but should not be employed for gudgeon pins and similar objects which are subjected to stresses as well as wear.

A Home Made Lubricant

Sir,—In the *Model Engineer* for April 28, there is a query about lard oil as a cutting lubricant, and a reference to the difficulty in obtaining supplies of it. Some years ago I read that lard oil was regarded as the best lubricant for screwing in steel, but that a 50−50 mixture of neatsfoot oil and paraffin was an excellent substitute. I tried this and have used nothing else ever since. I was once given some "proper" cutting oil for use with eight parts of water added and it is not in the same street as the neatsfoot−paraffin mixture.

New Zealand   K.J. Robinson
(September 1955)

Planishing Sheet Metal

C.D. Palmer (December 1935)

When beating out a sheet of thin metal, such as tin, to flatten it, I have always found it useful to lay the metal on a flat metal surface such as an anvil, and to cover it with a sheet of fairly thick cardboard, such as that used in shoe boxes, and to hammer the cardboard.

Provided that the hammer is kept reasonably square to the work, there is no fear of denting or damaging the surface of the metal.

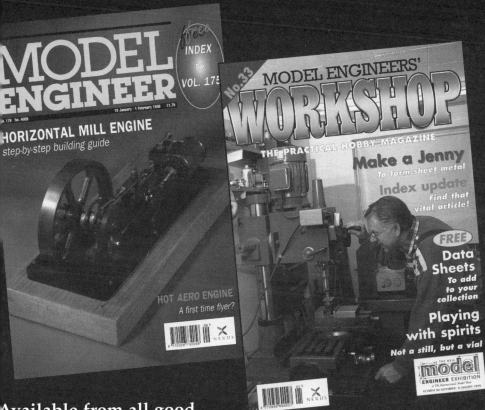